TECHNICAL ILLUSTRATION

TECHNICAL ILLUSTRATION

Second Edition

T. A. Thomas

DEPARTMENT OF DRAFTING
EL CAMINO COLLEGE
CALIFORNIA

FOREWORD BY
Carl L. Svenson

McGraw-Hill Book Company

New York   St. Louis   San Francisco
London   Toronto   Sydney

The illustrations of Problems: Group 1 (Probs. 1-1 to 1-51) are from *Graphic Science* by
French and Vierck, second edition, © 1963 by McGraw-Hill, Inc. Used by permission
of McGraw-Hill Book Company.

PREFACE

The second edition has been completely rewritten and contains valuable added information obtained by an extensive research trip covering the entire United States, Mexico, and parts of Canada. Many of the additions and revisions reflect important data acquired on this trip. In addition to hundreds of personal contacts in industry and education, correspondence with many authoritative people has contributed fresh information for this revision. Several important chapters have been added, and numerous typical problems with suggested assignments are included to provide for both beginning and advanced students.

This book has a threefold purpose: to serve as a text for classroom students and a practical guide for technical illustration educators; to function as a ready reference or handbook for technical illustrators, commercial artists, technical writers, engineers, and designers; and to be used as a book for home study. It is recommended for classes in schools and colleges, both public and private.

The techniques and procedures described here have been successfully tested in classes where students were being trained for positions as technical illustrators.

A special effort has been made to use familiar words and phrases of the trade and to write in a concise manner that would appeal to interested readers of this book.

Technical illustrations are not intended to be exact drawings like orthographic projections, and dimensions are seldom obtained by scaling an illustration. The main purpose is to show a representative picture of objects and provide better communication to the viewer. Any industry that designs, manufactures, repairs, maintains, installs, or sells a product profits from technical illustration, and the techniques and equipment used are basically the same, regardless of the industry.

This book presents an impartial review of industry's most frequently used practical techniques and methods: In some cases these techniques may not agree entirely with exact theory, but they are in common use and are entirely satisfactory. Each company has its favorite methods, adapted to the needs of the work at hand, and companies do not always agree in every detail on the techniques to be used. Variations in techniques are presented here to acquaint the reader with the existing requirements of industry and the technical knowledge and basic art ability needed, with emphasis on practical application.

This entire book is devoted to technical illustration. There is little discussion of orthographic projection, lettering, geometric construction, or fundamentals of drafting. Many good books about drafting such as *Mechanical Drawing* by French and Svensen, *Graphic Science* by French and Vierck, and *Engineering Drawing* by Zozzora, cover these subjects intensively. It should be understood, however, that a technical illustrator must thoroughly understand orthographic projection, blueprint reading, and other phases of drafting in order to successfully learn technical illustration. An extensive survey has shown that over 80 percent of the work of a technical illustrator is the preparation of line illustrations, and 91 percent of these line illustrations are drawn from blueprints.

One of the basic requirements for teaching a technical illustration course is problems. This book includes many typical orthographic drawings which are suitable for the beginner and the advanced student, from simple single details to complex assemblies.

Employment opportunities in the field of technical illustration are increasing, and there is an urgent need for qualified people.

The main difference between a basic, intermediate, and advanced course is the difficulty of the problems involved. Simple detail problems should be used in a basic course, with the intermediate student solving small subassemblies. The advanced student can progress to the more complex assemblies. Basic techniques of construction, thorough training in the use of ellipse and hexagon templates, technical freehand sketching, and simple shading should be taught in the very beginning courses. Basic courses should be restricted to isometric drawing with a very limited amount of oblique drawing, since reliable statistics show that less than one-tenth of 1 percent of technical illustrations are made in oblique. Students can advance to dimetric, trimetric, and perspective drawing in more advanced courses. Advanced courses should also include thorough instruction in the use of special equipment, such as the spring template, grids, the isometric ellipse protractor, and inking equipment. Techniques necessary for the solution of off-axis problems involving inclined planes, compound angles, double rotations, sections, and intersections should be reserved for the advanced student.

A student need not follow exactly the order in which material is presented in this book. In fact it is almost impossible to study material presented in one chapter without referring to material and methods presented in other chapters.

A thorough understanding of ellipse templates is probably the most important part of technical illustration, and considerable space has been allocated to this instruction. The use of other special equipment, such as the hexagon template, the spring template, the isometric ellipse protractor, and proportional dividers, must also be thoroughly understood if one is to become a successful technical illustrator.

To the educators who are contemplating courses in technical illustration or to those who have existing courses, I would be happy to send useful material for the cost of preparation and mailing. I welcome your inquiries for course outlines, solutions to problems in this book, and other related material. Feel free to contact me if I can be of assistance.

Grateful appreciation is expressed to many people in industry, as well as to former students, for their contributions and suggestions in the preparation of this book. To the many hundreds of people whom I interviewed on my research trip, go special thanks.

Particular thanks go to the following: Don Murphy and Robert Strum, North American Aviation, Inc.; Clifford Dickson, Ford Motor Co.; Crosby Barnes, TRW Systems; Richard Hallagan, Fisher Body Div., General Motors Corp.; V. J. Unks, Caterpillar Tractor Co.; Earle Posten, Douglas Aircraft Co., Inc.; Douglas Tubbs, General Dynamics Corp.; P. C. Armentrout, Boeing Airplane Co.; A. D. Kline, Western Electric Co.; Robert Rosequist, Motorola, Inc.; A. O. Pardoe, Raytheon Co.; and Jack Lowery, Chrysler Corp.

To Carl L. Svensen, well-known author of drafting books and recognized authority in the field, special appreciation is expressed for writing the foreword to this book.

Personal thanks are extended to my wife Verna for her untiring efforts and assistance and to Betty, Don, Ted, Mitch, and Sharlene for their moral support, which contributed immeasurably to the completion of this book.

T. A. Thomas

FOREWORD

Graphic communication by pictorial views has been man's most valuable means of description throughout the ages and has been adapted to many purposes. Great inventions have been described by a form which has become known as *technical illustration*. It was used by Leonardo da Vinci to describe his flying machine and his many other inventions.

The advent of the engineering age has made it necessary in the field of technical illustration to apply graphic communication and use it with greater exactness. The need for exact description which can be clearly read and understood in a minimum of time has developed a close integration of engineering and artistic ability. The resulting dual profession requires the reading of blueprints (engineering drawings), an understanding of shape and space description, and the ability to make a variety of pictorial views accurately so that parts and assemblies of parts can be readily identified.

Technical illustration is, therefore, an exact kind of graphic communication, made necessary by the complexity of machines, automobiles, aeronautical vehicles, and other engineering accomplishments. The need for well-prepared technical illustrators is so great and the supply so inadequate that a comprehensive and reliable presentation of the requirements and how to meet them has become a matter of vital importance. This volume meets the existing critical need by supplying a practical treatment of technical illustration. The author, T. A. Thomas, is particularly well qualified, for teaching and for applying his knowledge in industry, by virtue of his broad education, study, and experience; his extensive practice in the profession of technical illustration; his knowledge of the requirements of the aeronautical and other industries through personal interview and research all over the country; his long teaching experience, study, and valuation of the results of methods of teaching technical illustration; his contributions to education in technical illustration through preparation of plans, directions, and advice for numerous courses taught under different conditions by others; and his continuous research in all phases of technical illustration.

Technical illustrations are numerous and varied, and uses are constantly increasing. They are used to picture and identify separate parts, to show the arrangement of parts in whole or in part assembly, as production illustrations to facilitate putting parts together or taking them apart, for instructions in operation or servicing, and for many other purposes in all fields of industry.

Mr. Thomas has provided a complete and authoritative volume which gives a direct and practical treatment with understandable illustrations to explain the principles of technical illustration and which shows how to apply them to the requirements of industry.

Carl L. Svenson

CONTENTS

TECHNICAL ILLUSTRATION

1 WHAT IS TECHNICAL ILLUSTRATION?

[Technical illustration may be defined as drawing a view of an object in three dimensions according to blueprint specifications.] Primarily it is the translation of orthographic blueprints into three-dimensional drawings. This amounts to over 80 percent of the work of a technical illustrator.

The work of three-dimensional drawing is also known by such terms as production illustration, industrial illustration, technical art, perspective illustration, design illustration, and probably a few other titles.

The purpose of this book is to present the methods of converting blueprints into three-dimensional drawings, which are widely used in industry.

Occasionally the technical illustrator derives the shape and size of an object from photographs instead of blueprints or from dimensions taken from the actual object. He sometimes performs other tasks, such as photo retouching, airbrush work, and schematic drawing, but his main work is the preparation of three-dimensional drawings. To do his work well, the technical illustrator must be proficient in the use of isometric, dimetric, trimetric, perspective, and schematic drawing techniques. Accuracy, speed, and a feeling for layout are qualities needed by the illustrator.

Technical illustrations are not intended to be exact drawings like orthographic drawings. Dimensions are seldom obtained by scaling an illustration, although dimensions are sometimes shown on the illustration. The main purpose of technical illustration is to show a representative three-dimensional picture of an object.

Numerous minor variations in technique are used in industry, as the information that follows will show.

USES OF ILLUSTRATIONS

[Technical illustration has been called "the eyes of science and industry."] It is used by any industry that designs, sells, manufactures, repairs, or maintains a product. Generally speaking, technical illustrations are used for proposals, for presentations, or for publications.

Accurate three-dimensional drawing, as distinguished from freehand commercial art, has many uses. Industry has found that technical illustration can accelerate production and reduce costs.

Technical illustrations which show separate parts and huge assemblies can easily be understood even by those with limited knowledge of blueprints. Shop personnel, for instance, are often found using technical illustrations in their work. Aircraft and automotive operational handbooks, as well as maintenance and repair manuals, use the tools of technical illustration widely. By means of "exploded" drawings, these manuals clearly show the desired assembly and placement of parts, as well as the relationship of one part to another, as illustrated in Fig. 1-1: An illustrated parts breakdown (IPB).

Extensive use is made of technical illustrations to show a new design or to point up design changes on everything from fountain pens to airplanes. Illustra-

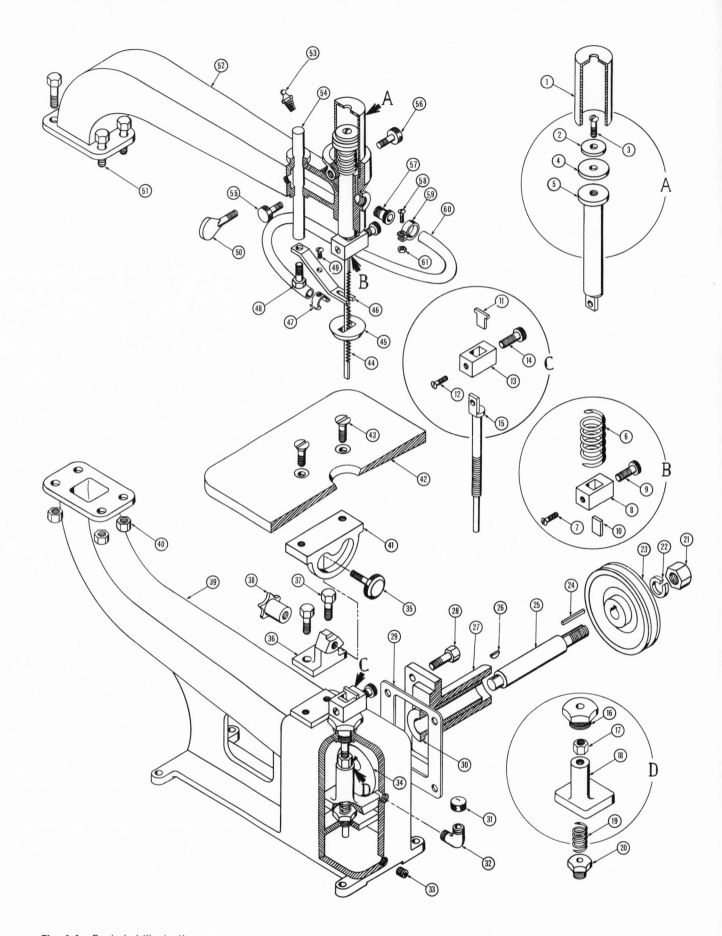

Fig. 1-1 Exploded illustration.

tions are also used in instructions that show assembly of do-it-yourself kits and the use of appliances and tools. Valuable use of technical illustration is made in acquiring new contracts and in preparing training aids for new personnel. Technical illustrators often work closely with technical writers by preparing drawings which the writers can study.

Technical illustration is relatively new; full use of this medium did not occur until World War II, when the aircraft industry began to utilize it extensively. Since that time, technical illustration has expanded rapidly to all types of industry, which are now vitally dependent on its tools.

TYPES OF ILLUSTRATIONS

[Basically, there are two distinct divisions of technical illustration: the engineering illustration and the publications illustration.]

Engineering illustrations are made for installations, manufacturing, design, production, and proposals for contracts. Usually they are assembly-type illustrations and, as the name implies, are used mainly by the engineering department. Engineering illustrations have few frills and are not meant to be works of art but to show a clear, accurate picture drawn closely to the requirements of the blueprints.

Publications illustrations are used for parts catalogs, maintenance and repair manuals, assembly manuals, structural repair manuals, flight handbooks, operations manuals, charts, and sales catalogs. The publications group may also have the job of preparing company handbooks or manufacturers' sales catalogs, where cartoon sketches, airbrush work, life drawing, and photo retouching may be required. This type of work is usually assigned to those with commercial art ability.

Publications illustrations do not always require blueprint accuracy but rather emphasize the eye appeal of the object or the relationship of one part to another and are usually the exploded type of illustration (see Fig. 1-1). Because of this more frills are added: shades, shadows, and perhaps color. Complete accuracy is not of prime importance, although proper proportion is maintained, and for this reason considerable "eyeballing" is used. [Eyeballing is the technical illustrator's term for drawing *approximately* to size and shape.]

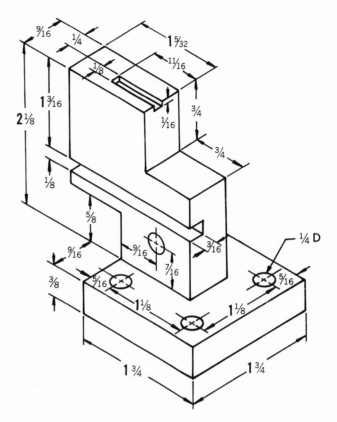

Fig. 1-2 Dimensioned illustration.

There is an increase in the use of technical illustrations on blueprints with orthographic, multiview drawings. In numerous cases, technical illustrations showing dimensions (Fig. 1-2) are being used or advocated for detail drawings on blueprints. This method makes it possible for anyone to obtain dimensions and visualize the drawing without the technical knowledge of blueprint reading. Multiview, orthographic, conventional blueprints are not completely eliminated, but they may be replaced in many instances and certainly supplemented to aid in better communication. The illustration thus serves a dual function. It can be used as a blueprint, and, in addition, it can be used for any of the other conventional uses of illustrations, such as in parts catalogs, installation illustrations, operations manuals, or, as so effectively demonstrated, in do-it-yourself drawings. Several different examples of technical illustrations are shown in this chapter.

TYPES OF ILLUSTRATORS

There appear to be two general groups of illustrators: the illustrator who has the required technical ability to read complex blueprints and the illustrator who possesses a good art background but who lacks good blueprint-reading ability. A definite distinction exists between these two, and they are referred to here as a _technical illustrator_ and a _technical artist_, although their occupational titles vary in industry.

[The technical illustrator is one who has a thorough knowledge of blueprints and has had a comprehensive course in drafting—one who has the ability to visualize and draw an object accurately in three dimensions from complex blueprints. He is well qualified to do engineering-type illustrations but may lack natural art ability, proficiency in cartoon work and life drawing, and knowledge of shades, shadows, and color. He may not understand airbrush work or photo retouching, and his inking technique may be poor.

The technical artist may be deficient in the knowledge of complex blueprints but may possess good natural art ability. He understands shades, shadows, color, cartoon work, and life drawing. He is a proficient inker and possibly has some ability in the use of the airbrush and photo retouching. The technical artist has more commercial art ability than the technical illustrator. He relies more on drawing a freehand, or proportional, picture than an accurate scale drawing. This type of individual would be more suited to publications work than engineering, since more eyeballing is normally done for publications and more commercial art ability is therefore desirable.]

DESIRED QUALIFICATIONS

The most competent illustrator, obviously, is one with a combination of the above-mentioned qualities. In order to reach the peak of success, an illustrator must have a good knowledge of drafting as well as a thorough understanding of basic art. Since he works mainly from orthographic, detail, and assembly drawings, it is imperative that he complete a comprehensive course in drafting or advanced blueprint reading to prepare him for technical illustration. In other words, to learn his job thoroughly, the student of technical illustration must first know orthographic projection and have a working knowledge of blueprints.

IMPORTANCE OF TECHNICAL SKETCHING

A successful technical illustrator must be adept at freehand technical sketching as well as drawing mechanically to scale. He must be proficient in freehand work in order to plan a preliminary layout of his work. In most cases a problem must be roughed in freehand before the accurate drawing is started. Valuable use of freehand technical sketching is also made to convey the thoughts and ideas of engineers, designers, and technical writers.

Freehand technical sketching is valuable, too, when a drawing must be made for which no blueprints are available. A freehand sketch is made, and dimensions are obtained directly from the object and placed on the sketch. The illustrator must therefore thoroughly understand the use of measuring devices and be able to obtain dimensions from the object itself.

Because it is so valuable to the technical illustrator, freehand technical sketching is treated separately in Chap. 2.

PROCEDURE FOR PREPARING ILLUSTRATION

The five steps of a general procedure that the illustrator should follow in preparing a technical illustration are listed below (some of these steps may vary in different illustration groups):

1. Study the blueprints, photograph, or engineering sketch.
2. Make a freehand technical sketch to plan the layout.
3. Prepare the accurate illustration, called the _rough_ or _construction_ drawing.
4. Trace the finished illustration.
5. Do _paste-up_ work.

In the first step, obtain the blueprints from the files and make a thorough study of the problem. In some cases a problem may be drawn from a photograph or rough sketch instead of blueprints, and occasionally an illustration is drawn by using the actual object as a reference. Be sure you understand what you are to draw.

In step 2, prepare some type of freehand technical

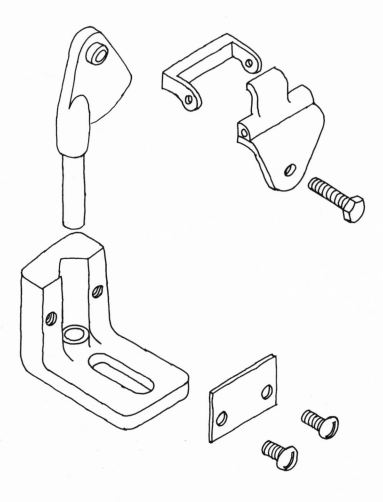

Fig. 1-3 Freehand sketch.

sketch (Fig. 1-3), although it is not always required. Check the sketch with the supervisor, the writer, or the designer. The freehand sketch will aid you in visualizing the problem. It will aid in making the proper layout and placement on the page and will serve as a check to see that all parts are included in the drawing. The freehand sketch, which may be merely a few scribble notes, will save many hours and considerable money by helping to avoid errors, omission of parts, and improper layout.

In step 3 you make the accurate drawing—called the rough or construction drawing—mechanically (see Fig. 1-4). The good appearance of a finished illustration depends on careful construction work in this step. The illustration should be placed in the most descriptive position so that it can easily be understood. Proper spacing should be maintained, especially on exploded drawings. Illustrations should be reduced to a number of geometric forms. Center lines can then be located, and exact overall dimensions

can be measured for each part along these center lines. In some cases the rough or construction drawing is not made complete. For example, when duplicate parts are to be shown, such as bolts, nuts, or washers, sometimes only one is drawn and then this one drawing moved into the desired positions and traced the required number of times on the finished illustration. This will ensure uniformity for the duplicate parts. Some illustrators place only center lines for ellipses and hexagons on the rough and then draw the complete hexagon or ellipse on the finished illustration. Irregular-shaped objects may be "boxed in" and formed by drawing geometric shapes and locating key points, which can be followed on the finished illustration. Numerous construction lines are needed, and because most problems require many hours of work, the drawing becomes badly soiled. Since it is almost impossible, in most cases, to erase all construction lines and soiled spots, step 4 becomes necessary. Tracing the illustration may be eliminated,

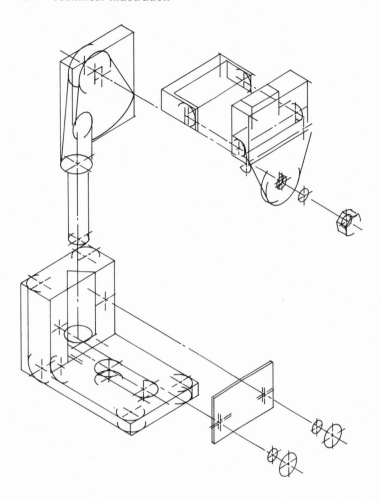

Fig. 1-4 Rough or construction illustration.

however, when a nonprint pencil is used. This nonprint pencil, makes a blue or purple line which does not reproduce on a blueprint machine. The object lines of the problem are "heavied up." Only these lines will show on the reproduction.

In step 4 the illustration is usually traced (Fig. 1-5) on a clean sheet of vellum, tracing cloth, Strathmore paper, or drafting film in pencil or ink. When the problem is traced, the illustrator has the opportunity to make adjustments for any mistake in layout made in step 3 by merely moving the rough into proper position. In some cases a problem is drawn on Strathmore paper or illustration board directly or by tracing with carbon paper. A 2H pencil or a harder one is used most frequently on the finished illustration to obtain sharp lines and to avoid excessive graphite on the paper. The pencil with the plastic-type lead is also used in tracing on drafting film. This pencil resists smudging and in some cases makes a darker line. Some difficulty is experienced however in

keeping the point sharp. The illustrator should remember that many illustrations are reduced in size, and therefore proper line width must be maintained in order to reproduce satisfactorily. The pencil should be rotated slowly between the fingers in order to obtain sharp uniform lines.

In step 5, which is usually called paste-up, finished illustrations are often placed on mountboard, and an overlay is made of vellum or acetate. An accuracy check, or "tech" check, is then made, and corrections can be placed on the vellum overlay. Paste-up may also include the placement on the illustration of commercial material such as Artist-Aid (Fig. 1-1). The finished drawing is then submitted for revisions or corrections and final approval.

Drawings made on Strathmore paper, vellum, tracing cloth, illustration board, or drafting film are often inked in preparation for reproduction. The technical illustrator should be capable of making a neat ink drawing in addition to sharp pencil drawings.

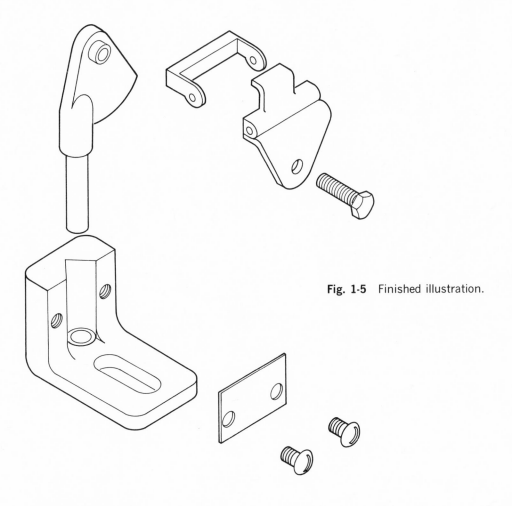

Fig. 1-5 Finished illustration.

DRAFTING FILM

Drafting film (Mylar), mentioned in the preceding section, is a polyester film base which is waterproof and practically indestructible. It is used in many cases as a drawing surface for technical illustration and drafting.

Plastic leads are normally used with drafting film, although in some cases the regular graphite lead, lithoprint pencils, or ink are used. Lines made with plastic lead are practically smearproof. Some plastic leads used on film are washable, and, if so, a soiled illustration may be carefully washed without destroying the lines. Nonwashable plastic leads are also available. Plastic leads can be obtained in various degrees of hardness. Mars has K1, K2, K3, K4, and K5. The K1 is the soft grade, and K5 is the hardest. The K3 is about the same as a 2H graphite lead.

Plastic lead requires a different technique from that used with the graphite lead. The recommendations

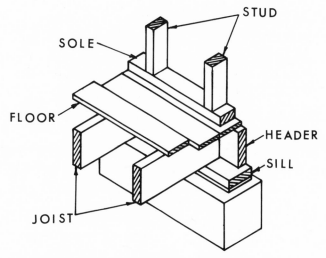

Fig. 1-6 Architectural illustration.

of the manufacturer should be checked in order to obtain satisfactory results. Some helpful hints will be found at the top of page 10.

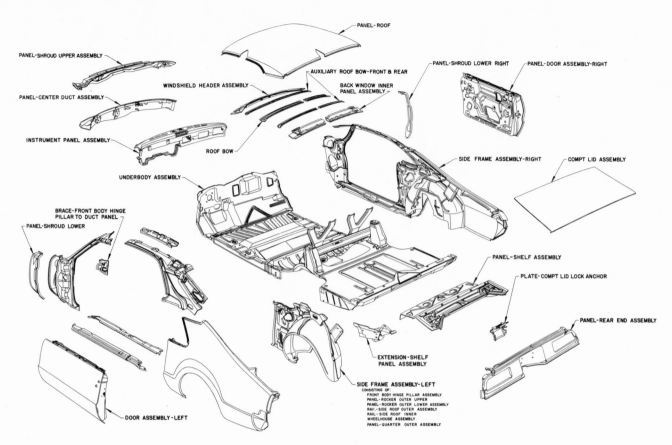

Fig. 1-7   Automotive body illustration.   (Fisher Body Div., General Motors Corp.)

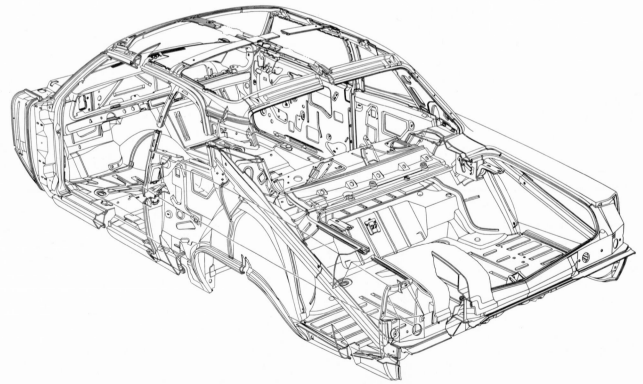

Fig. 1-8   Automotive body illustration.   (Fisher Body Div., General Motors Corp.)

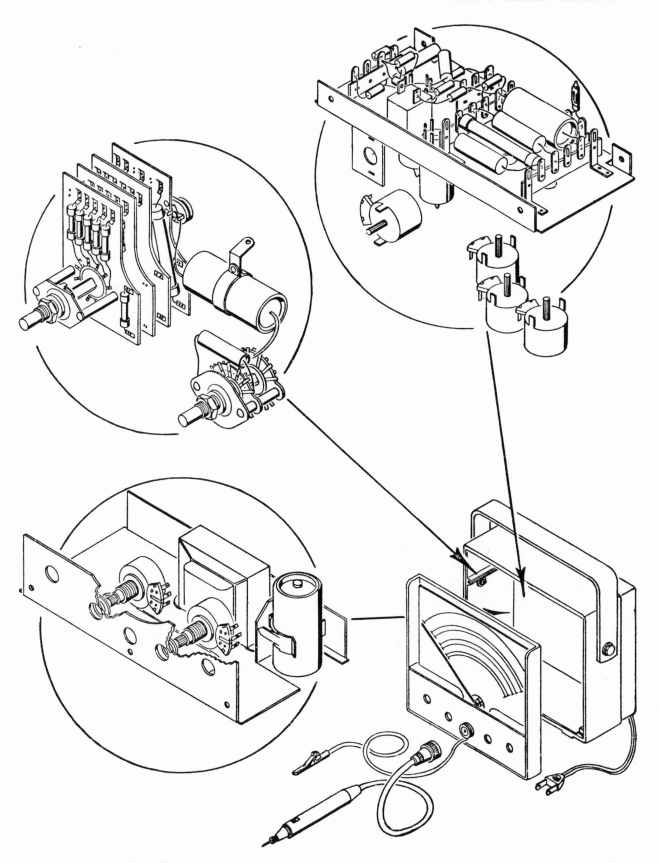

Fig. 1-9 Electronic illustration.

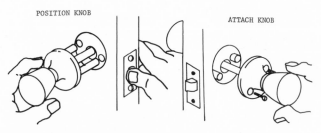

Fig. 1-10 Installation illustration.

Fig. 1-11 Presentation illustration. (TRW Systems, Co., Don Stever.)

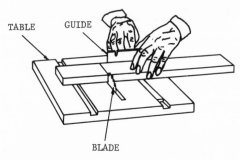

Fig. 1-12 Operations illustration.

1. The surface must be free of finger marks or grease spots. Clean with soap and water and use Pounce or light erasing, especially when using ink.
2. Special vinyl erasers are used when removing pencil or ink lines. For stubborn lines, particularly ink lines, moisten the eraser lightly. There are also some liquid cleaners available.
3. Draw with a lighter touch when using the plastic pencil than when using the graphite one. A slightly blunt point is recommended.
4. There are a number of special inks available for drawing on film. Regular inks are not satisfactory.

ILLUSTRATION SPECIFICATIONS

Illustrations made for the military services are governed by specific regulations or military specifications, which must be carefully followed. These regulations vary, depending upon the military service for which the illustration is prepared. Thorough knowledge of the "mil specs" is essential in order to prepare a satisfactory illustration.

Definite specifications or standards are also required for many nonmilitary illustrations, such as those established by The Air Transport Association of America.

REPRODUCTION METHODS

After the final drawing is completed, it is ready for reproduction. Technical illustrations are reproduced in several different ways, and skill in line technique and neatness are extremely important. Many of the drawings are photographed and reduced in size. Most drawings are made to a larger scale and then reduced in final form. Many are made "twice up," which means that they will be reduced to half the size of the original illustration. Other reductions are used, such as "$1\frac{1}{2}$ up." In some cases original illustrations may be enlarged.

The technical illustrator should be familiar with the more common methods of printing technical illustrations. Many techniques are used in reproducing technical illustrations, but probably the most common are the offset and the letterpress methods.

In the offset method (see Fig. 1-13), the illustration,

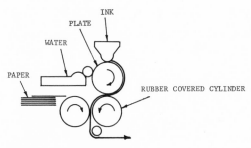

Fig. 1-13 Offset printing.

printed material, and photographs, if included, are usually mounted on a stiff cardboard backing. A picture is taken with a special camera, and a negative is produced. The picture may be reduced or enlarged. In most cases it is reduced in size. Corrections are made on the negative as required by opaquing light spots or even cutting it apart with scissors. Stripping operations are completed in final preparation for making a plate. The negative is placed on a plate, usually metal, although sometimes paper, and is exposed to a bright light and developed. The plate is chemically treated so that only the lines, printed material, or photographs, appear.

In the final preparation, the plate is attached to a metal cylinder and inked, and the illustration is then transferred to a rubber blanket on a cylinder from which the illustration is printed. The chemicals on the surface of the plate are such that the ink will adhere only to the illustration. The smooth, clear surface of the plate resists the ink and picks up a water coating fed from a water supply tank. The water cleans the plate but does not affect the ink. The paper passing between the offset cylinder and the impression cylinder picks up the inked image carried on the rubber blanket cylinder. The ink is transferred from the flat surface of the plate to the rubber blanket and finally to the paper. An exact duplication of the illustration is the result.

In the letterpress method (Fig. 1-14) ink is trans-

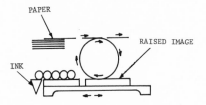

Fig. 1-14 Letterpress printing.

ferred from a raised surface directly to the paper. This raised surface may be type, engravings on metal, wood, rubber, or a combination of different materials. A good example of letterpress is the raised rubber stamp, which is inked and pressed on the paper to reproduce the raised image. The paper is fed to the press. The press, which may be flat or rotary, is inked, and the inked image is reproduced directly on the paper.

The silk-screen process uses a transfer of ink through the mesh of silk or other similar material directly to the paper. The image is either handcut or photographically prepared and attached to the screen. The ink is forced through the mesh of the silk by a squeegee passing across the surface of the screen. The prepared image does not allow the ink to pass through the mesh of the screen, and this results in the reproduction of the image.

Xerography, an electrostatic process, is a widely used reproduction method in technical illustration work.

Blueprints and bluelines are made for temporary purposes, such as checking illustrations, and for engineering use.

DRYMOUNT

Technical illustrations are sometimes covered by a protective coating and permanently fastened to a mountboard by means of the Drymount process. A thin sheet of shellac is laminated to the illustration by means of a fusing process in which pressure and heat are applied by a mechanical device.

BLUEPRINT ANALYSIS

The primary job of a technical illustrator is the translation of orthographic blueprints into three-dimensional illustrations as shown by Figs. 1-15 to 1-21. These illustrations show orthographic views of various-shaped objects and the translation of these views into three-dimensional illustrations. The orthographic views have been placed in a three-dimensional plane in order to show their relationship to the illustration. The purpose is to assist the reader to visualize the object and to show the transition from the blueprint views to the technical illustration. This in no way suggests that technical illustrations be made by placing orthographic views on the drawing and then projecting from these views.

A successful technical illustrator must completely understand orthographic blueprints in order to accomplish this translation, because over 90 percent of line illustrations are made from blueprints.

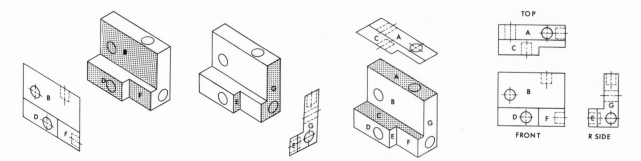

Fig. 1-15   Blueprint analysis.

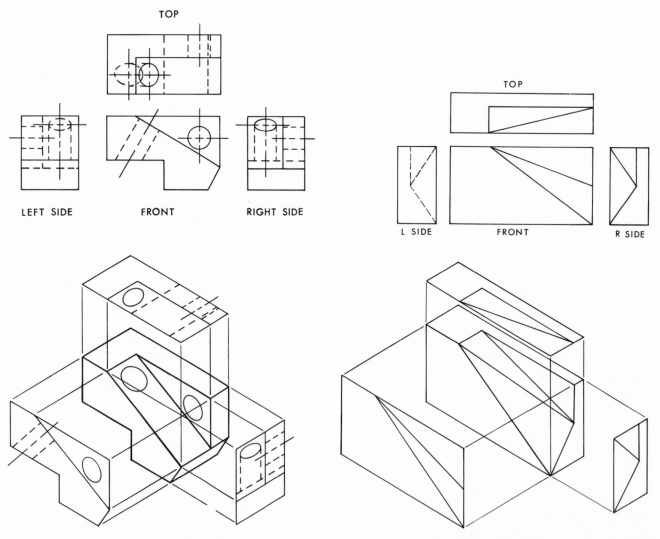

Fig. 1-16   Blueprint analysis—inclined plane.

Fig. 1-17   Blueprint analysis—oblique plane.

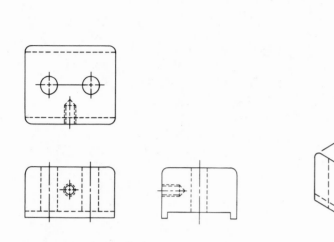

Fig. 1-18 Blueprint analysis.

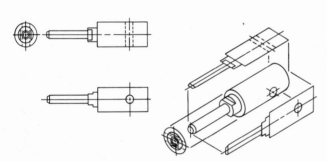

Fig. 1-19 Blueprint analysis—cylindrical object.

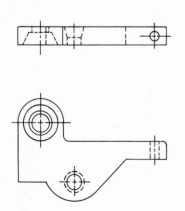

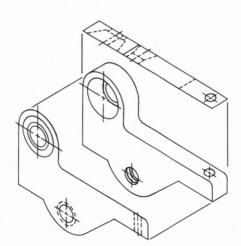

Fig. 1-20 Blueprint analysis.

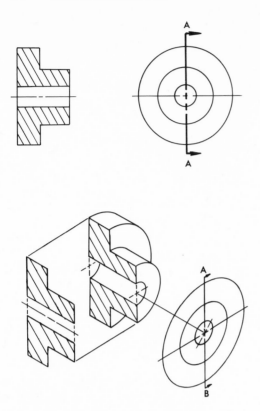

Fig. 1-22 Presentation illustration. (TRW Systems, Co., Don Stever.)

Fig. 1-21 Blueprint analysis section.

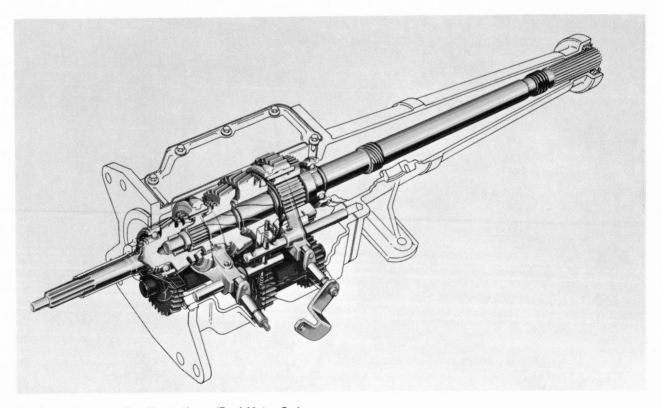

Fig. 1-23 Cross-section illustration. (Ford Motor Co.)

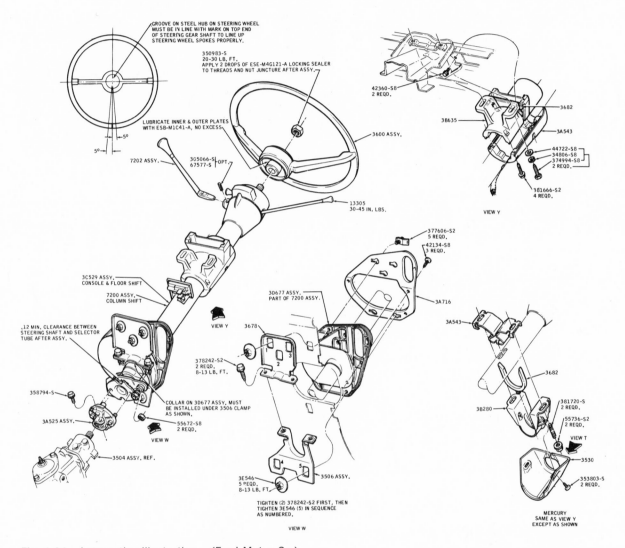

GROOVE ON STEEL HUB ON STEERING WHEEL MUST BE IN LINE WITH MARK ON TOP END OF STEERING GEAR SHAFT TO LINE UP STEERING WHEEL SPOKES PROPERLY.

350983-S
20-30 LB. FT.
APPLY 2 DROPS OF ESE-M4G121-A LOCKING SEALER TO THREADS AND NUT JUNCTURE AFTER ASSY.

LUBRICATE INNER & OUTER PLATES WITH ESB-M1C41-A, NO EXCESS.

3600 ASSY.

7202 ASSY.

305066-S } OPT.
67577-S

5°
5°

13305
30-45 IN. LBS.

42360-S8
2 REQD.

3682
3B635
3A543
44722-S8
34806-S8
374994-S8
2 REQD.
381666-S2
4 REQD.

VIEW Y

3C529 ASSY.
CONSOLE & FLOOR SHIFT

7200 ASSY.
COLUMN SHIFT

.12 MIN. CLEARANCE BETWEEN STEERING SHAFT AND SELECTOR TUBE AFTER ASSY.

358794-S

3A525 ASSY.

3504 ASSY. REF.

VIEW Y

3D677 ASSY.
PART OF 7200 ASSY.

3678

378242-S2
2 REQD.
8-13 LB. FT.

COLLAR ON 3D677 ASSY. MUST BE INSTALLED UNDER 3506 CLAMP AS SHOWN.

55672-S8
2 REQD.

VIEW W

377606-S2
5 REQD.
42134-S8
3 REQD.

3A716

3A543

3682

3B280
381720-S
2 REQD.
55736-S2
2 REQD.

VIEW T

3530

353803-S
2 REQD.

3E546
5 REQD.
8-13 LB. FT.

3506 ASSY.

TIGHTEN (2) 378242-S2 FIRST, THEN TIGHTEN 3E546 (5) IN SEQUENCE AS NUMBERED.

VIEW W

MERCURY
SAME AS VIEW Y
EXCEPT AS SHOWN

Fig. 1-24 Automotive illustration. (Ford Motor Co.)

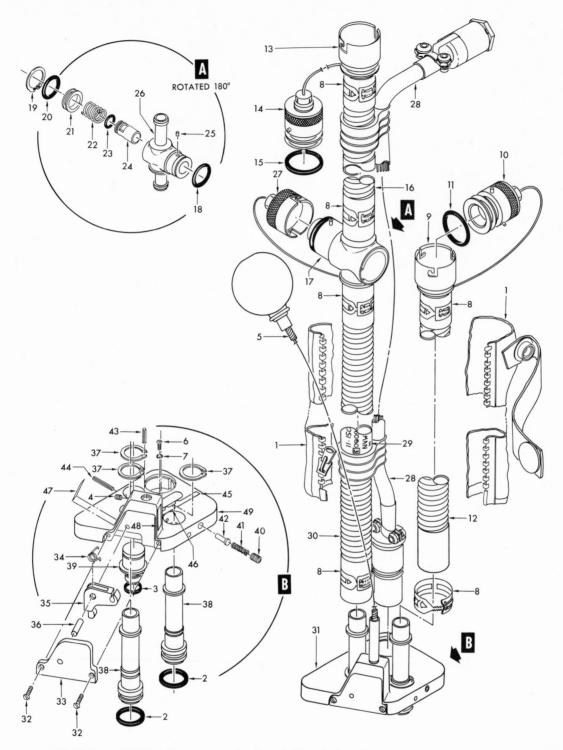

Fig. 1-25   Group-assembly illustration.   (Lockheed Aircraft Corp.)

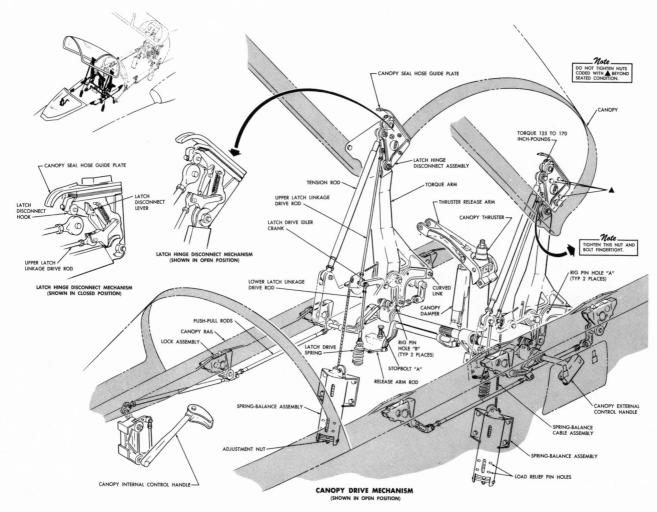

Fig. 1-26   Canopy-drive illustration.   (Northrop Corp.)

PROFESSIONAL ASSOCIATIONS

The Technical Illustrators Management Association (TIMA) is an international organization for technical illustrators and teachers of technical illustration. Other national and local organizations also provide guidance and promote and improve technical illustration. These include the Society of Engineering Illustrators, the National Association of Industrial Artists, the Society of Technical Writers and Pub-

lishers, the Association of Technical Artists, etc.

Every technical illustrator should be associated with some professional organization in the field.

AUTOMATION IN ILLUSTRATION

Automation has entered the technical illustration field. Figure 1-27 shows the computer-directed Illustromat 1100, an automatic device for preparation of technical illustrations. (See page 18.)

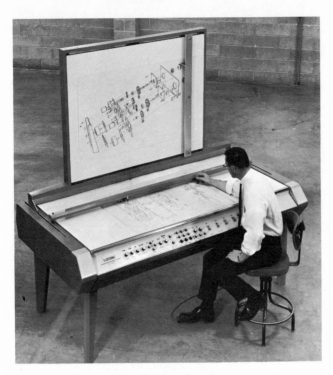

Fig. 1-27 The Illustromat 1100. Computer Graphics Instrument. (Perspective, Inc.)

Questions

1. Define technical illustration.
2. What are some of the uses of technical illustration?
3. What is eyeballing?
4. Name two distinct divisions of technical illustration.
5. What is the difference between these two divisions?
6. What are exploded drawings?
7. Why is freehand technical sketching important?
8. What are the basic steps for preparing an illustration?
9. What is meant by twice up?
10. Discuss the steps used when preparing an illustration.
11. What is a rough or construction drawing?
12. What is IPB?
13. Explain the difference between offset and letterpress.
14. What is the purpose of Drymount?
15. What is drafting film?

2

FREEHAND
TECHNICAL SKETCHING

One of the basic requirements of a technical illustrator is the ability to do freehand sketching. The finished illustrations are, of course, made with the aid of mechanical equipment, but the well-qualified illustrator must master freehand methods as well. In most cases the illustrator is first required to make a freehand sketch of each problem, and in some cases the freehand sketch itself is touched up and used for the final illustration. Since the technical illustrator often works with technical writers, engineers, and designers, he is sometimes required to make a three-dimensional sketch of an object which is located away from the drafting room and in a place where mechanical equipment cannot be used. It is therefore obvious that freehand technical sketching is of prime importance in technical illustration.

Serious thought and considerable time should be given to the freehand sketch in order to plan the proposed drawing thoroughly. The sketch is practically useless unless it is made properly, and if done properly, it will actually save time when the finished drawing is to be made.

The preliminary planning of a problem must be done freehand, because it is much easier to make a correction on a freehand sketch than it would be to redraw a complete, finished problem. In this way the proper layout on the finished drawing is ensured.

In order to do freehand sketching, the illustrator must know the different systems of making three-dimensional drawings and be familiar with basic

techniques. For this reason, before freehand sketching is attempted, reference should be made to Chaps. 3 to 5, which discuss basic techniques and various systems used in sketching.

SKETCHING SUGGESTIONS

Every illustrator will develop his own methods of freehand technical sketching; however, certain fundamental suggestions are offered here which should be helpful. A soft lead pencil, H or F, is desirable for sketching, and in some cases a litho grease pencil may be used. The pencil should be held a greater distance from the point than for normal writing. This allows the illustrator to see the lines plainly as they are drawn and permits a greater movement of the pencil point without changing the position of the wrist. The pencil should be moved lightly over the paper by means of a series of short strokes, rather than with one continuous movement. After the sketch is completed, the lines can be "heavied in" where needed.

SKETCHING STROKES

In drawing a line it is suggested that overlapping strokes be used. In the case of a long line, a stiff arm movement will be more effective than finger movement. Finger movement with the wrist stationary is probably more suitable for short lines, curves, circles, or ellipses. When a straight line is drawn, the eye should be concentrated on the point of termination of the intended line rather than on the pencil point. It is easier to make a straight line in this way. Normally it is better to draw lines with a movement away from the body from left to right for a right-handed illustrator and, of course, the opposite for a left-handed person. Move the paper, if necessary, in order to place it in the most desirable position. Sometimes it is helpful to rotate the paper in order to draw slanting or irregular lines. Care should be taken, however, that the proper axis of the drawing is maintained.

HOW TO SKETCH THE ELLIPSE

Sketch the ellipse by using four strokes as illustrated in Figs. 2-1 and 2-2. Draw a center line and locate points on this line to represent the minor-axis distance of the ellipse. Draw another center line perpendicular to the first, and locate points on this line to represent the major axis of the ellipse. The ellipse can then be sketched passing through these four points on the center lines.

The ellipse may be sketched by drawing a box with center lines for the major and minor axis as shown in Fig. 2-3. Cylinders are also shown with the proper

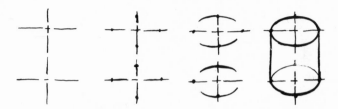

Fig. 2-2 Sketching cylinder.

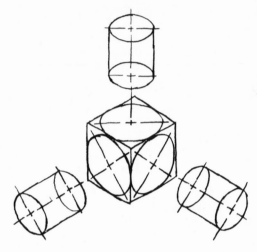

Fig. 2-3 Alignment of ellipse.

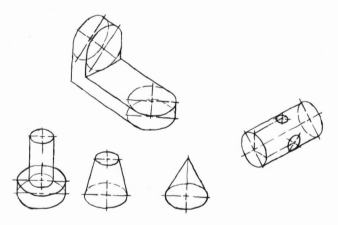

Fig. 2-4 Ellipse-sketching problems.

alignment of the ellipse. Other examples involving the ellipse are shown in Fig. 2-4. The most important point to remember about the ellipse is that the minor axis should be aligned with the axis of the hole or shaft, as discussed in Chap. 4.

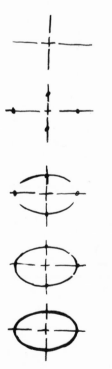

Fig. 2-1 Sketching ellipse.

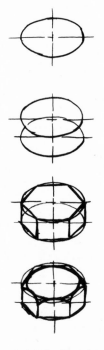

Fig. 2-5 Sketching hexagon.

HOW TO SKETCH THE HEXAGON

Hexagons may be easily sketched freehand by first using one of the methods described above to lightly sketch an ellipse and then inscribing the hexagon as indicated in Fig. 2-5. The chamfer may be deleted, and sometimes the square sides are eliminated. Reference should be made to Chap. 4 for helpful hints.

BOXING-IN CONSTRUCTION

Figure 2-6 shows a step-by-step method using a boxing-in construction. First, enclose the part with a box and cut the box apart to form the general shape; second, make the center lines for the holes and arcs; third, sketch the holes and arcs; and fourth, complete the tangents and heavy-in the object lines of the part.

CENTER-LINE CONSTRUCTION

Figure 2-7 shows a step-by-step sketch using a center-line method of construction. First, draw the

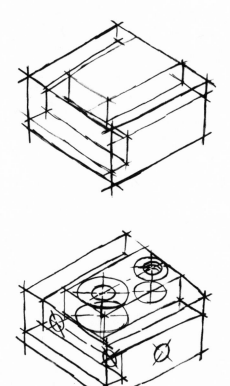

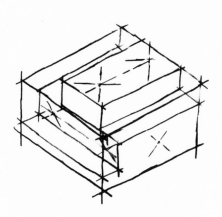

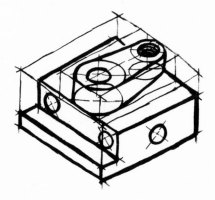

Fig. 2-6 Steps in sketching—boxing in.

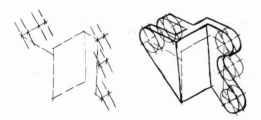

Fig. 2-7   Steps in sketching—center line.

center lines; second, make the ellipses, arcs, fillets, and rounds; and third, complete the tangents and straight lines and heavy-in the object lines.

PROPORTION IN SKETCHING

One of the most important points in sketching is to maintain proportion.   One method that can be used to accomplish this is a system of diagonals.   Figure 2-8 illustrates a satisfactory procedure to follow.

MAIN PURPOSE OF SKETCH

There are three main reasons for the freehand sketch: (1) to analyze the blueprints, actual part, or photograph, (2) to plan the layout, and (3) to be sure all parts are shown in an assembly.

LAYING OUT THE SKETCH

In making a sketch in the illustration room, mechanical equipment such as the ellipse and hexagon templates can be utilized.   Isometric, dimetric, and perspective grids can be placed beneath the sketching paper as a guide, and in some cases the sketch may be made on grid paper.   The Andersen perspective board (Fig. 10-9) is very useful in making a perspective sketch.   Use of mechanical equipment in technical sketching will depend upon the accuracy desired and whether the drawing is made where such equipment is available.   In any case the illustrator should be skilled in making the sketch entirely freehand whenever necessary.   The freehand technical sketch is normally made by the same method of illustration (isometric, dimetric, perspective) as that planned for the finished drawing.   If grids are not used, the proper axis of the sketch may be established.   After the axis is established for the sketch, the object should then be boxed in with a light line by drawing a three-dimensional box equal in size the the greatest dimensions of the object (see Fig. 2-6).   This large box

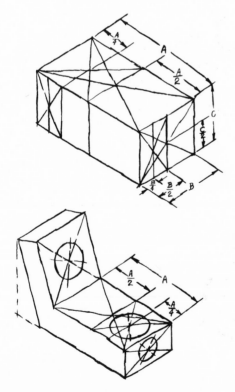

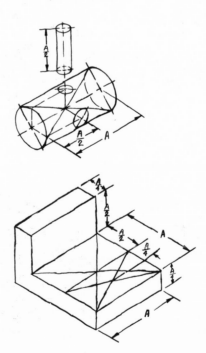

Fig. 2-8   Proportion in sketching.

may then be subdivided into smaller geometric forms. The sides of the box are drawn parallel to the axis of the drawing. If more than one part is to be drawn, which is generally the case, a box may be drawn for each part, except for round or cylindrical parts such as bolts and nuts. In the case of exploded drawings, center lines should be drawn in order that the relationship of one part to another can be shown properly. After the part or parts are boxed in, center lines can be drawn to be used as guides for bolts, nuts, washers, holes, shafts, and circular items, as shown in Fig. 2-9.

Even though actual measurements are not made on a freehand sketch, good proportion should be maintained.

Steps in Layout. Figure 2-9 is a typical freehand technical sketch. It shows an exploded view of a simple assembly. Use the following procedure to sketch this problem: First study thoroughly the detail and assembly blueprints. In this example an isometric axis is chosen to be used for the sketch. Next draw a three-dimensional box using light lines. Sketch the box large enough to enclose the part completely. A complete layout of an assembly can be made more easily by selecting a major part located near the center of the assembly. After this part is boxed in, the other parts can be located around it

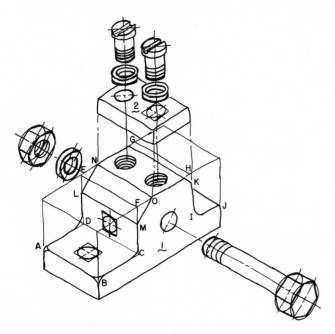

Fig. 2-9 Exploded freehand sketch.

in their proper position. The large box is then subdivided by adding lines *AB*, *AD*, *BC*, *DC*, *DE*, *CF*, *GH*, *HI*, *IJ*, and *JK*. The edge *EF* is then eliminated by adding the sloping lines *OM* and *LN*. The two new edges *LM* and *NO* are then drawn. Round the square corners at *C* and *D* to form fillets. Round the corner at *H*, and draw another line tangent to this curve, upward and to the left. Add curved lines at corners *A* and *B* to show that edges *AB*, *AD*, and *BC* are rounded. Line *BC* is not eliminated even though this is a round edge, because without the line the surface could not be identified. Short curved marks on this edge may be used instead of the line, but this is seldom done.

After the general shape of the object is established, draw center lines to locate the holes. Draw the ellipses for the holes using one of the methods described previously. The illustrator can select the method desired, including use of the ellipse template whenever possible. Extend construction lines upward from the corners of the top of large part 1. Draw the lower surface of part 2 so that it does not overlap the top of part 1. In some cases parts are overlapped as long as no important detail is covered; likewise part 2 may sometimes be drawn in position against the top of part 1. Complete the outline of part 2 by extending center lines upward from the holes in part 1. Draw center lines for the holes, and sketch ellipses on part 2. Locate the bolts and washers for part 2 by sketching center lines upward from the holes in part 2. Draw the round-head bolts along these center lines. Locate the large "hex"-head bolt along a center line drawn from the hole in the large part 1. Determine the length of the bolt and add a vertical center line at these points. Draw an ellipse at the threaded end, using center lines as before. Only half of the ellipse will show. Draw the hex head of the bolt by first drawing a large ellipse and then inscribing the hexagon within it. Remember that the hex head is drawn so that the shortest distance across the flats is aligned with the axis of the bolt. This is the way hex templates are used (see Chap. 4, the section on the use of hexagon templates), and the hex looks best when placed in this way, as shown previously. Another hex is then drawn in order to show the thickness of the hexagon head. Chamfer is sometimes added on the hex.   The flat washer and hex nut are then added on the opposite side of part 1 and in line with the hole.   Visible lines are then heavied in to complete the sketch.

Questions

1. Why is technical sketching important?
2. With whom does the technical illustrator work?
3. What kind of pencil is recommended for sketching?
4. Describe a method for drawing a freehand line from one point to another.
5. What mechanical aids are sometimes used in freehand sketching?
6. Describe a method for drawing a freehand ellipse.
7. Give a simple way to make a freehand hexagon.
8. What is meant by boxing in?
9. What are the main purposes of a freehand sketch?

Exercises

FREEHAND SKETCHING

Select problems from the end of Chap. 3 (Group 1) and make freehand sketches of these selected problems.

Use a soft lead pencil, H or F, and begin by making a rectangular box enclosing the entire object with light lines.   Proceed by cutting the box apart in order to form the general shape.   If the object has round holes, draw a line to represent the minor axis of the ellipse and then draw a line perpendicular to the minor-axis line to represent the major axis.   Place points on these lines that locate the minor- and major-axis distance. Sketch the ellipse.   Be careful to maintain proper porportion and refer to Fig. 2-8, which shows a diagonal system for obtaining measurements.   Connect tangents to ellipses if needed and darken the object lines.   Refer to Figs. 2-1 to 2-7 for suggested techniques.

3 ISOMETRIC DRAWING

Isometric drawing is one type of axonometric drawing. Dimetric and trimetric drawings are also axonometric drawings, and they are discussed in Chap. 11. An isometric drawing is a three-dimensional drawing made with the receding axes drawn at 30° from the horizontal. True measurements are made along the three axes, and only one scale is needed for measurements.

If a box is revolved 45° and then tilted forward so that the angle between the line of sight and the horizontal plane is approximately 35°16′ (see Fig. 3-1), it is isometric. The isometric view of a box, a projection of the side view of this box, and the manner of obtaining the angle of the line of sight are shown in Fig. 3-1. In isometric drawings all the angles formed where the three edges of a box meet at a corner are 120° (see Fig. 3-2).

An isometric drawing is about $1\frac{1}{4}$ times larger than a true representation. This is illustrated in Fig. 3-3, which shows a 1″ isometric cube, but one with ellipses about $1\frac{1}{4}$″ across the major axes. A true isometric representation of the cube would appear as in Fig. 3-4, where 35° ellipses are 1″ across

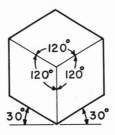

Fig. 3-2 Regular isometric.

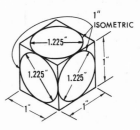

Fig. 3-3 Isometric drawing.

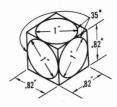

Fig. 3-4 Isometric projection.

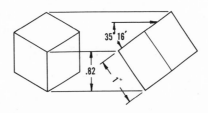

Fig. 3-5 Isometric-projection theory.

the major axes. Notice that the scale along the axes is reduced to 0.82″. The explanation for this foreshortened scale is represented in Fig. 3-5. This is known as an *isometric projection*. Isometric projection is rarely used, and instead, true scale is used

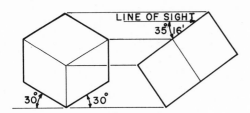

Fig. 3-1 Isometric line of sight.

along the axes. This method is called *isometric drawing* (Fig. 3-3).

Since isometric drawing is $1\frac{1}{4}$ times larger than true, the isometric ellipses must be $1\frac{1}{4}$ times larger than true, as indicated in Fig. 3-3. (See Chap. 4.)

The 1-in. 35° ellipse is used on the surfaces of Fig. 3-4, but this results in a foreshortened scale. In other words, the isometric ellipse is the same as the 35° ellipse except that it is $1\frac{1}{4}$ times larger than the indicated diameter. This is explained thoroughly in Chap. 4.

Isometric is the most frequently used method for making three-dimensional drawings. There are several variations of the conventional isometric drawing. The regular method, which is the most common, pictures the object from the top (see Fig. 3-6, view 4). The reversed-axis method shows the bottom view of an object (see Fig. 3-7). The long-axis method (Fig. 3-8), which revolves the axis, is used mainly for long-shaft-type assemblies, although it may be used for a special view of any object.

A step-by-step illustration of the orthographic problem is shown in Fig. 3-6. Numbered lines and lettered points of the orthographic views are placed in their proper location on the isometric illustration.

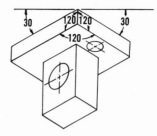

Fig. 3-7 Reversed-axis isometric.

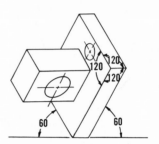

Fig. 3-8 Long-axis isometric.

ISOMETRIC LINES

Isometric lines are lines that are along the axes or parallel to the axes of the isometric drawing. True measurements can be made only along isometric lines or parallel to these lines, and this is one of the main advantages of isometric drawing. Isometric lines are shown in Fig. 3-9. An orthographic view of the problem is given with the numbered lines which can be measured true distance on the isometric drawing.

NONISOMETRIC LINES

Nonisometric lines are inclined lines that cannot be measured. They are lines that are neither along the axes nor parallel to the axes of the isometric drawing. In Fig. 3-10, line 8 is a nonisometric line. It cannot be measured, but must be plotted as indi-

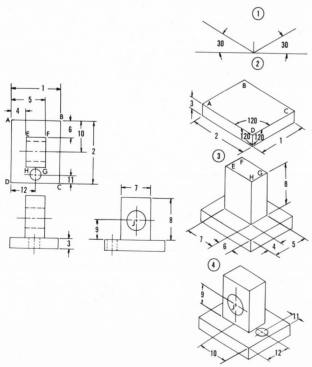

Fig. 3-6 Isometric-drawing solution.

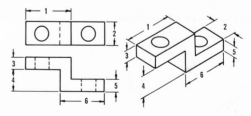

Fig. 3-9 Isometric lines.

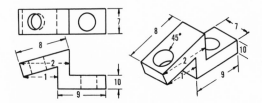

Fig. 3-10 Nonisometric lines.

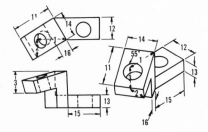

Fig. 3-11 Nonisometric lines—oblique plane.

cated by line 2. Lines 7, 9, and 10 are examples of isometric lines that can be measured. Figure 3-11 shows a problem with a compound angle and the isometric solution. Lines 11, 14, and 16 are examples of nonisometric lines, which must be plotted to determine their length, as indicated by lines 1, 2, and 3. Another useful method for determining the length of nonisometric lines utilizes the ellipse as a measuring device. It is explained in Chap. 7.

Notice that the holes on the nonisometric planes in Figs. 3-10 and 3-11 are made with the angle-size ellipses 45 and 55°. The isometric ellipse can be used only on isometric planes. (See Chap. 7.) The

method for determining the angle-size ellipse for inclined planes is explained in Chap. 7.

When using the angle-size ellipses on nonisometric planes, the desired diameter must be multiplied by $1\frac{1}{4}$ since an isometric drawing is $1\frac{1}{4}$ times larger than a true representation. This is demonstrated in Fig. 3-12, which shows the orthographic view of an object with an inclined plane and the isometric solution. A 50° angle-size ellipse is the proper ellipse for this inclined plane. One illustration shows the 1-in. 50° ellipse, which is obviously too small. The other illustration confirms the fact that a $1\frac{1}{4}$-in. 50° ellipse must be used on this 1″ nonisometric plane.

When using the Hexangle template on nonisometric planes, multiply the diameter size of the desired hexagon by $1\frac{1}{4}$ in the same manner as the ellipse template. This is illustrated in Fig. 3-13. In this case, however, the 45° hexagon is used since this is the nearest available size to 50°.

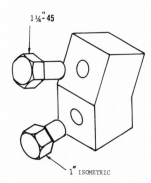

Fig. 3-13 Nonisometric hexagon size.

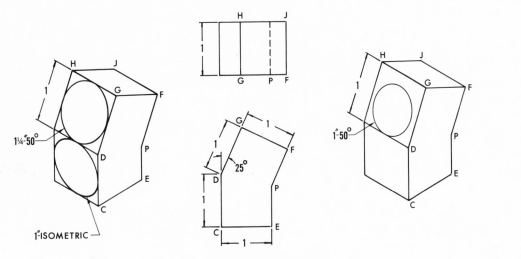

Fig. 3-12 Nonisometric ellipse size.

28   Technical Illustration

BOXING-IN METHOD OF CONSTRUCTION

In order to draw irregular-shaped objects, the box method of construction is used. The measurements can be made only along the three axes or parallel to the axes.

The orthographic views of an object are shown in Fig. 3-14, view *A*. An isometric box is drawn large enough to enclose the object completely (view *B*). Coordinate points are used to find the points of the irregular object. Since some of the lines are not parallel to the isometric axes, they cannot, therefore, be measured. Lines that are not parallel to the isometric axes are called *nonisometric lines*. It is necessary sometimes to make construction lines on the orthographic views in order to obtain these coordinate points.

To locate point *C* on the isometric view, measure on the vertical axis distance 1, and then measure distance 2 along a 30° line. Point *A* is located on the isometric view by measuring distance 3 as indicated, along the vertical axis, then measuring distance 4 along a 30° line. Points *E* and *D* are located by measuring distance 5 along the 30° axis and then distance 6 on a vertical axis. Figures 3-15 and 3-16 show other examples of the box-method construction. In Fig. 7-9, an example is shown of a coordinate-point layout involving intersection of cylinders.

The method for drawing angles and ellipses and other techniques in isometric drawing are explained in Chaps. 7 and 9.

The mechanical aid called the *isometric ellipse*

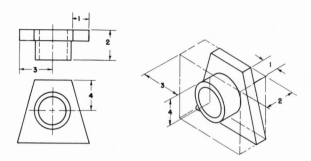
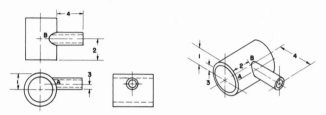

Fig. 3-15 Isometric problem solution—boxing.

Fig. 3-16 Isometric intersection—center line.

protractor is sometimes used to find angles and is described in Chap. 6.

REVERSED-AXIS ISOMETRIC

Reversed-axis isometric is a variation of regular isometric and is used to show a bottom view of an object. Instead of being drawn upward, the 30° receding axes are drawn downward. A drawing using the reversed-axis method is shown in Figs. 3-17 and 3-7.

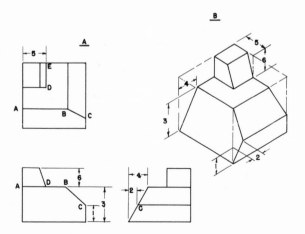

Fig. 3-14 Isometric problem solution—boxing.

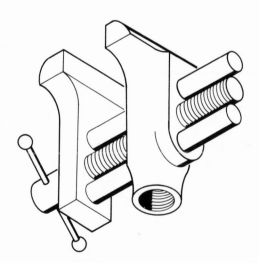

Fig. 3-17 Reversed-axis isometric illustration.

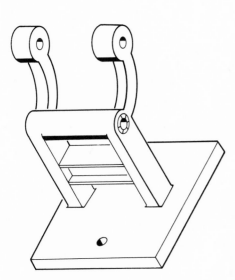

Fig. 3-18 Long-axis isometric illustration.

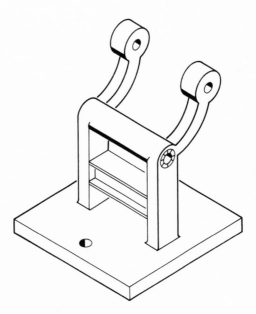

Fig. 3-19 Regular isometric illustration.

LONG-AXIS ISOMETRIC

An example of long-axis isometric is shown in Fig. 3-18. Compare this drawing with Fig. 3-19, which shows the same object by using the regular isometric method. The long-axis isometric drawing is recommended when there is a series of washers, gaskets, bushings, nuts, and bolts to be shown. Vertical lines are drawn at a 60° angle with the horizontal (Fig. 3-8). The use of the isometric ellipse template in long-axis isometric varies slightly from the way it is used for regular isometric or reversed-axis isometric. The minor axis of the ellipse is aligned with the horizontal axis when drawing ellipses on vertical surfaces. When drawing ellipses on horizontal surfaces the minor axis of the ellipse is aligned with the 60° axis as shown in Fig. 3-18.

ISOMETRIC GRIDS

Some technical illustration departments in industry use a grid for making isometric drawings and freehand sketches, as shown in Fig. 3-20. The grid is placed under the drawing paper so that the illustrator can follow the isometric lines. Measurements are obtained by counting the isometric squares, which are properly scaled on the grid. The grid is a handy aid, especially for those who lack a complete knowledge of isometric theory.

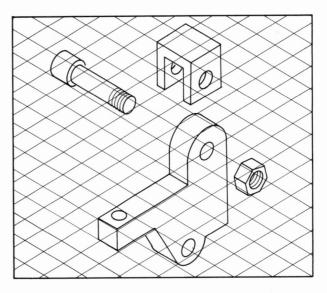

Fig. 3-20 Isometric grid.

Questions

1. Define isometric drawing.
2. Name three types of isometric drawings.
3. What foreshortened scale is used when making an isometric projection?
4. Explain boxing-in method of construction.
5. What type isometric is used to show the bottom of an object?
6. What are isometric lines?
7. What are nonisometric lines?

PROBLEMS: GROUP 1
Basic Problems

Select problems from the group shown below and make isometric drawings of each problem. Make drawings of the same problems that were used for freehand sketches. Compare the shape and size of the drawings with the freehand sketches that you made.

Draw problems using regular isometric, reversed-axis, and long-axis. Place the objects in the most desirable position for showing the most important characteristics of the problem.

Draw construction lines lightly, using regular lead or the blue or purple construction pencils discussed in Chap. 1.

Darken the object lines to complete the illustration. Refer to Fig. 3-6 and Figs. 3-14 to 3-16, and study Chap. 4 when ellipses must be drawn.

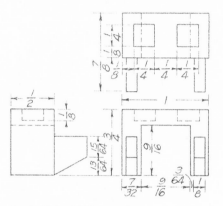

Prob. 1-1   Skid mount.

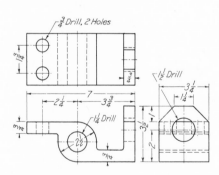

Prob. 1-4   Bracket.

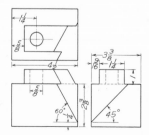

Prob. 1-8   Wedge block.

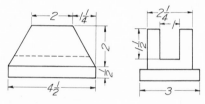

Prob. 1-2   Guide block.

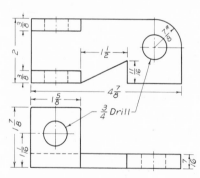

Prob. 1-5   Hinged catch.

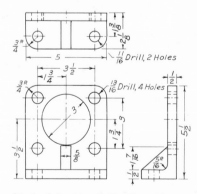

Prob. 1-9   Head attachment.

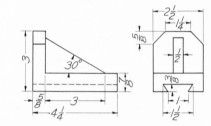

Prob. 1-3   Dovetail stop.

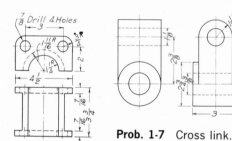

Prob. 1-6   Bearing.   **Prob. 1-7**   Cross link.

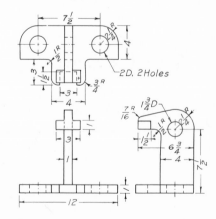

Prob. 1-10   Slide stop.

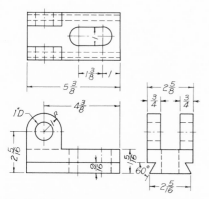

Prob. 1-11   Dovetail bracket.

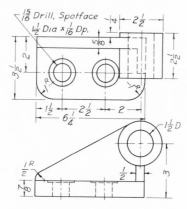

Prob. 1-12   Offset bracket.

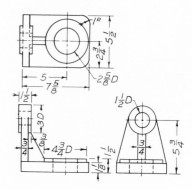

Prob. 1-13   Cradle bracket.

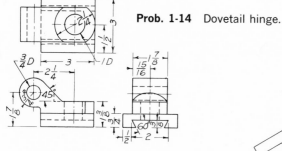

Prob. 1-14   Dovetail hinge.

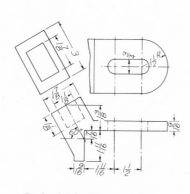

Prob. 1-16   Strut anchor.

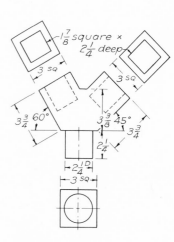

Prob. 1-17   Strut swivel.

Prob. 1-15   Cable clip.

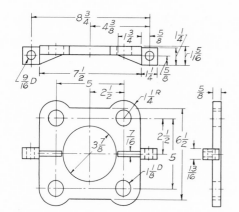

Prob. 1-18   Tie plate.

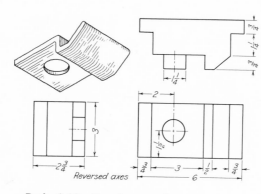

Prob. 1-19   Forming punch.

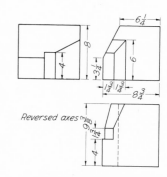

Prob. 1-20   Springing stone.

ISOMETRIC SECTIONS

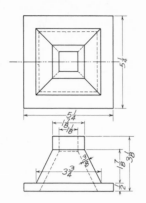

Prob. 1-21 Column base.

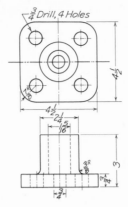

Prob. 1-22 Base plate.

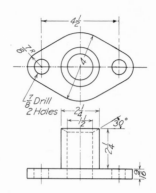

Prob. 1-23 Gland.

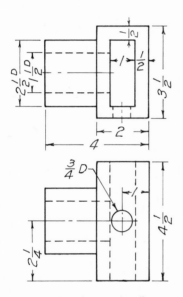

Prob. 1-24 Squared collar.

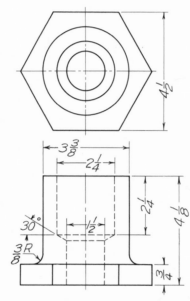

Prob. 1-25 Blank for gland.

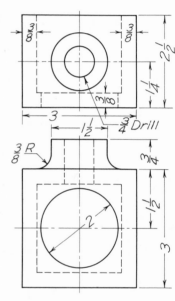

Prob. 1-26 Sliding cover.

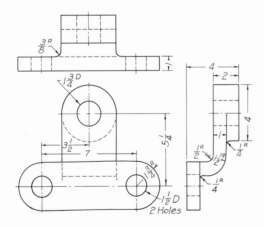

Prob. 1-27 Rod support.

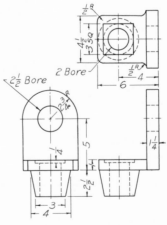

Prob. 1-28 Side-beam bracket.

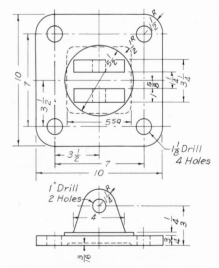

Prob. 1-29 Head yoke.

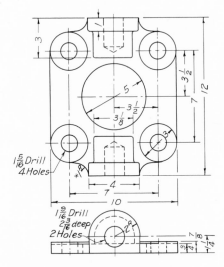

Prob. 1-30 Trunnion plate.

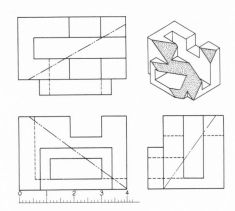

Prob. 1-31 Section study.

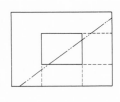
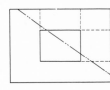

Prob. 1-32 Section study.

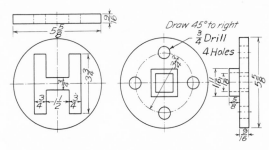

Prob. 1-33 Letter die. **Prob. 1-34** Guide plate.

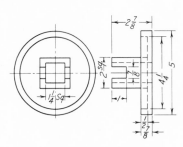

Prob. 1-35 Brace base.

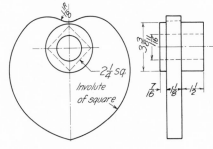

Prob. 1-36 Heart cam.

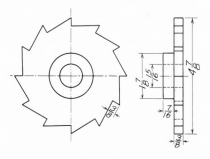

Prob. 1-37 Ratchet wheel.

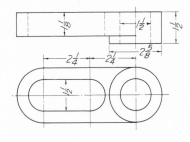

Prob. 1-38 Slotted link.

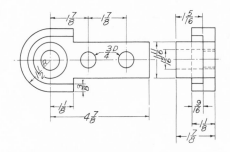

Prob. 1-39 Swivel plate.

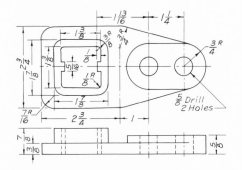

Prob. 1-40 Slide bracket.

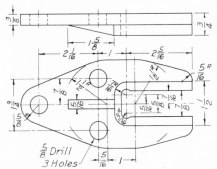

Prob. 1-41 Jaw bracket.

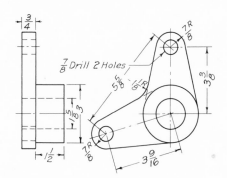

Prob. 1-42 Bell crank.

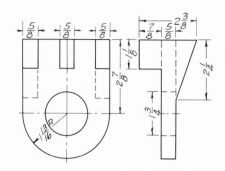

Prob. 1-43 Stop plate.

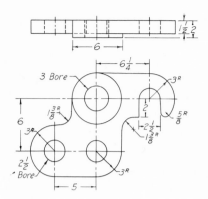

Prob. 1-44 Hook brace.

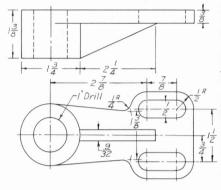

Prob. 1-45 Adjusting rod support.

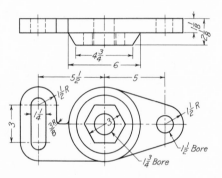

Prob. 1-46 Link.

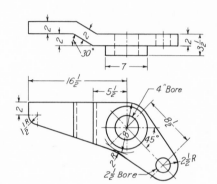

Prob. 1-47 Pawl.

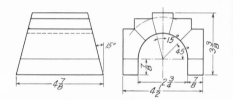

Prob. 1-48 Culvert model.

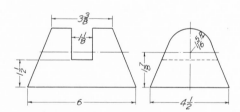

Prob. 1-49 Slotted guide.

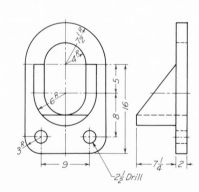

Prob. 1-50 Support bracket.

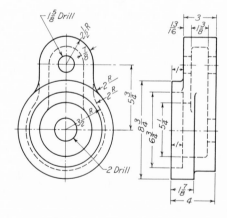

Prob. 1-51 Port cover.

4 THE ELLIPSE AND HEXAGON TEMPLATES

One of the most important things to learn in technical illustration is the use of the ellipse and hexagon templates. The illustrator is constantly using these mechanical aids in various ways, and it is important that their use be thoroughly understood. The most common errors made in technical illustration are due to improper use of the ellipse template.

THE ELLIPSE TEMPLATE

The ellipse template is primarily used to draw three-dimensional views of circles or circular objects. Actually the ellipse template is used in many ways: In some instances it may be used as a protractor or to determine foreshortened scales. This will be explained in the pages that follow. The ellipse template is also used for making fillets, rounds, and threads. In three-dimensional drawings the planes of horizontal and vertical surfaces are actually drawn oblique in relation to the plane of projection; therefore, circles or circular objects drawn on these surfaces are represented by ellipses (see Fig. 4-1).

Parts of the Ellipse. Before a discussion of the types of ellipse templates, it must be emphasized that the ellipse has two important parts: the minor axis and the major axis. The minor axis is the shortest axis across the ellipse, or the minor diameter. The major axis is the longest axis across the ellipse, or the major diameter (see Fig. 4-2).

There are numerous types of ellipse templates, which can be classified by two general names: the isometric ellipse and the angle ellipse template. The isometric ellipse is used only on isometric drawings, while the angle ellipse templates are used for orthographic, dimetric, trimetric, oblique, and perspective drawings. Nonisometric planes require the use of angle ellipse templates.

Isometric Ellipse Template. The isometric ellipse template (Fig. 4-3) is used on all isometric surfaces of an isometric drawing. There is an isometric projection ellipse template marked 35°16′, which is different from the usual isometric drawing template. The major difference is the length of the major axis. On the isometric drawing template the distance across the major axis is greater than the diameter of the circle that the ellipse represents, whereas on the isometric projection template the distance across the major axis is equal to the diameter of the circle to be represented. In other words, the isometric projection ellipse template has been foreshortened, which is the case in an isometric projection or when a foreshortened scale is used for isometric drawing, as discussed in Chap. 3 on isometric drawing.

Difference between Isometric Template and Angle Templates. There is one main difference between the isometric drawing template and the template for varied angles. On the isometric template, the distance across the major axis is greater than the diameter of the circle the ellipse represents (see Fig. 4-4a), and of course this makes the minor axis greater. Figure 4-4a shows the $\frac{9}{16}''$ isometric ellipse, although the actual distance across the major

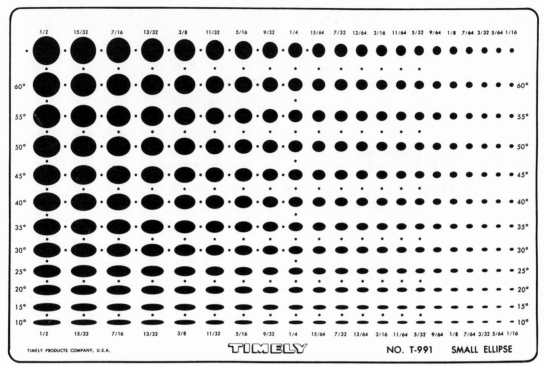

(a)

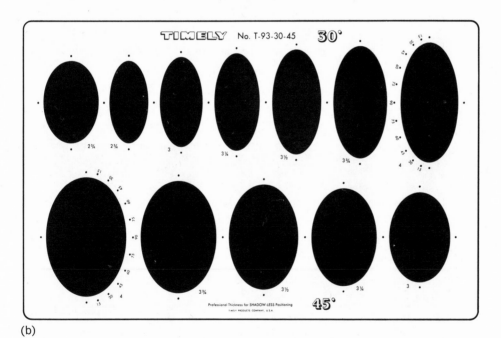

(b)

Fig. 4-1 Small angle ellipse template. (Timely Products Co.) (b) Large angle ellipse template. (Timely Products Co.) (c) Angle ellipse templates and large angle ellipse templates. (The Lietz Co.) (See facing page.)

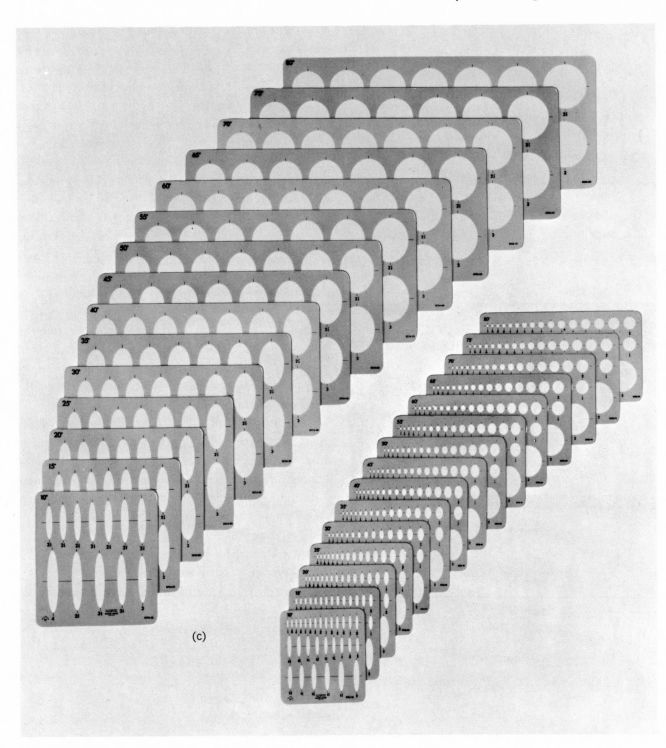

(c)

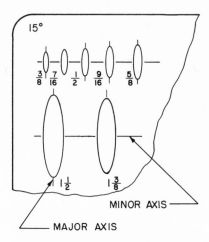

Fig. 4-2 Ellipse showing major and minor axis.

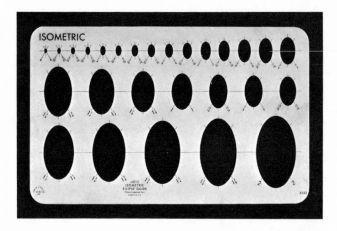

Fig. 4-3 Isometric ellipse template. (The Lietz Co.)

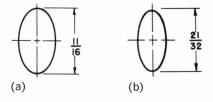

Fig. 4-4 (a) Isometric ellipse. (b) Angle ellipse.

axis is about $^{11}/_{16}''$, or about 1.22 times greater than the actual diameter indicated on the template. This is because normally no foreshortened scale is used in isometric drawings, and an object is about 1.22 times larger than a true representation should be. The minor diameter, or the distance across the minor axis of an isometric ellipse, is about 0.7 times the diameter of the circle that the ellipse represents.

Angle Ellipse Templates. On the angle ellipse templates (see Fig. 4-1) the distance across the major axis is equal to the diameter of the circle it represents (see Fig. 4-4b). This is true because of the foreshortened scale used on drawings where these ellipses are used. The distance across the minor axis of angle ellipse templates varies with the angle size. The smaller the angle size, the shorter the distance across the minor axis (Fig. 4-10). Angle ellipse templates may be purchased for every 5° from 10 through 80°. A small-size angle ellipse template with small ellipses for all the above angles is available with sizes varying from $^1/_{16}$ to $^1/_2''$. This template is a must since many small ellipses are drawn, and they must be accurate in order to avoid distortion. Large angle-size ellipse templates from 2'' to 4'' are shown in Figs. 4-1b and 4-1c. Jumbo ellipse templates may be obtained to 12'' in diameter (see Fig. 4-17). Some angle ellipse templates allow for the diameter of the pencil lead and may be slightly larger than the indicated diameter.

Proper Alignment of the Ellipse Template. The most important thing to remember when using any ellipse template is to align the minor axis of the ellipse with the axis of the hole or shaft. Figures 4-5 and 4-6 show how the ellipse is used in industry. When representing circles with the ellipse, the minor axis is always aligned with a line which represents a perpendicular to the plane of the surface on which the ellipse is to be drawn.

Common errors in the use of the ellipse template are illustrated in Fig. 4-7. Note the difference in appearance of the ellipses. The minor axis was not aligned with the axis of the hole or shaft and gives a distorted view.

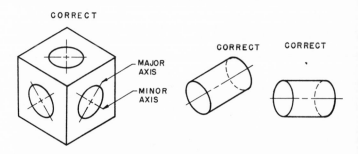

Fig. 4-5 Correct alignment of ellipse.

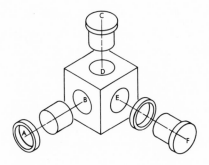

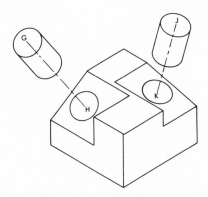

Fig. 4-6 Correct alignment of ellipse.

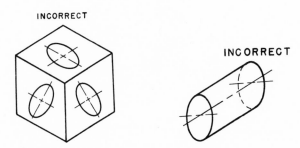

Fig. 4-7 Incorrect alignment of ellipse.

How to Find the Line of Sight. The correct angle-size ellipse for a given surface is one that is equal to the angle between the horizontal line of sight and the plane of the circle on the three-dimensional drawing, as illustrated in Fig. 4-8. This figure shows a three-dimensional drawing of a 1″ cube and merely illustrates the meaning of the term *line of sight.* A side orthographic view of the cube is drawn, and we find that the horizontal line of sight makes an angle of about 15° with the plane of the circle. The 15° ellipse should be used on the top surface of the three-dimensional drawing, since it is the nearest angle

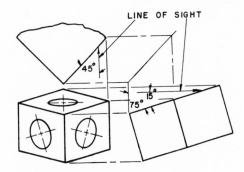

Fig. 4-8 Line-of-sight illustration.

to the actual angle between the line of sight and the plane of the circle. A partial top orthographic view is drawn of the cube, and we find that the line of sight made with the front vertical surface of the cube is about 45°. The 45° ellipse should be used for the vertical surfaces on the three-dimensional drawing, since it is the nearest ellipse to the actual line of sight.

Different Methods for Showing Angle Size. Some ellipse templates show the angle size as the angle between the plane of the circle and the vertical, as shown in Fig. 4-8. If the angle-size ellipse is shown in this way, a 15° ellipse would be shown as 75°and a 30° ellipse would be shown as 60°. In other words, the complement of the angle is used. Line of sight is also illustrated in the orthographic drawings in Fig. 4-9.

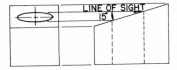

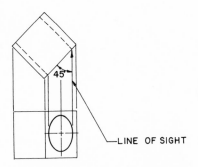

Fig. 4-9 Line-of-sight orthographic.

Distance across Minor Axis. Figure 4-10 shows how ellipses vary in distance across the minor axis. This figure illustrates that the greater the amount of surface shown, the larger the angle size of the ellipse.

How to Show a Vertical Hole on a Sloping Surface. A different procedure must be used if a hole is to be shown on a sloping surface such as *R* and *S* in Fig. 4-11. The actual shape of the hole is elliptical; therefore, since in technical illustration the ellipse represents a circle, it is technically incorrect to use the ellipse, and the shape of the hole must be plotted. The method for drawing such holes on sloping surfaces *R* and *S* is shown in Fig. 4-11.

The following procedure is for a vertical hole on surface *R*. The same general procedure is used for a horizontal hole on surface *S* except that the basic ellipse is different.

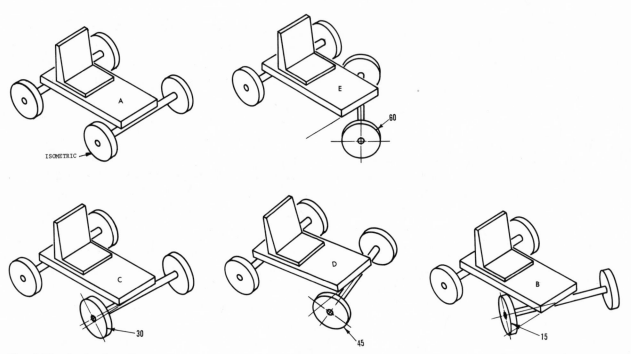

Fig. 4-10 Angle-size ellipse.

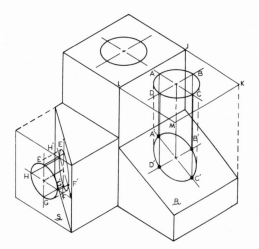

Fig. 4-11 Finding holes on sloping surface.

1. Draw construction lines *LM, JK,* and *KM* as though surface *R* were horizontal.
2. Draw the proper ellipse on the horizontal surface *LJKM.* In this case it is isometric.
3. Locate the major axis *A'C'* of the ellipse for the sloping surface.
4. Locate the minor axis *D'B'* of the ellipse for the sloping surface.
5. Locate the four points on the major and minor axis on the sloping surface by projecting down from the four points *ABCD* on the isometric ellipse.
6. Connect the four points on the sloping surface by using parts of an ellipse.

Eyeball Method. In some instances the length of the major axis of the ellipse on the sloping surface is determined from the orthographic blueprint, and then this length is drawn on the sloping surface of the three-dimensional drawing, as shown in Fig. 4-12. The distance *A* is equal to the distance *B*. The proper ellipse for this surface is made by drawing one-half of the ellipse and then moving the template along the major axis so that the template will coincide with the other point of location on the major axis. The result is an ellipse with the major axis stretched.

Nonisometric Ellipses. A diagram is shown in Fig. 4-13, picturing nonisometric ellipses. The outer ring of ellipses represents circular disks on center lines, as in an illustration of the end of a pipe or a wheel on a shaft. The figures accompanying the ellipses indicate the templates used to draw them. The figures reading in degrees on the directional arrows indicate the inclination of each adjacent center line from an isometric line. The isometric lines are heavier than the others, and the ellipses attached to

them are shaded. The inner ring of ellipses represents circles on square planes, such as would be developed by a hole through a flat surface; the inclination of each plane from an isometric norm is indicated by the line along the edge of the plane. When viewed so that title and description read normally, the graph shows center lines and planes revolving about a vertical axis, as pictured in the little figure in the lower right-hand corner. If the graph is turned so that one or the other of the inner corners becomes a base (note the double line and accompanying legend), it shows center lines and planes revolving about a horizontal axis, swinging to the right or left as shown by the little figure in the adjacent corner.

Ellipse Oddity. Occasionally problems arise in using the ellipse template when one ellipse must be shown concentric to another. An example is shown in Fig. 4-14, the ellipses are not truly concentric.

When one ellipse is placed concentric to another, the minor-axis distance *x* is not equal to the major-axis distance *y* (view 1). Some distortion occurs, as in the case of examples 2 and 3. Distance *BD* is obviously greater than *x*. To correct this, the small ellipse is made larger, as indicated by the dashed lines. This locates a more desirable distance *DF* and *CE*. A larger ellipse is used to connect *E* to *F*. The major- and minor-axis variations are demonstrated also in view 3. The large ellipse is not tangent to the small ellipse at point *A*. In this case the large ellipse can be moved slightly to form an arc tangent to the ellipse.

Plotting an Ellipse. Ellipse templates are manufactured for almost any size ellipse needed; however, they may not always be available, and occasionally it becomes necessary to plot an ellipse. The four-center method for plotting an ellipse is shown in Fig. 4-15. Use the following procedure:

1. Draw a three-dimensional square with all sides equal to the diameter of the circle.
2. Find the midpoint of each side.
3. From these midpoints draw lines perpendicular to each side of the square.
4. Where these construction lines intersect, points *A, B, C,* and *D* are the centers for arcs to be drawn by using a compass. This system can be used for all angle sizes of ellipses.

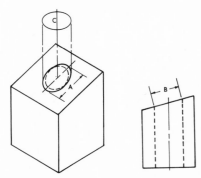

Fig. 4-12 Approximate hole on sloping surface.

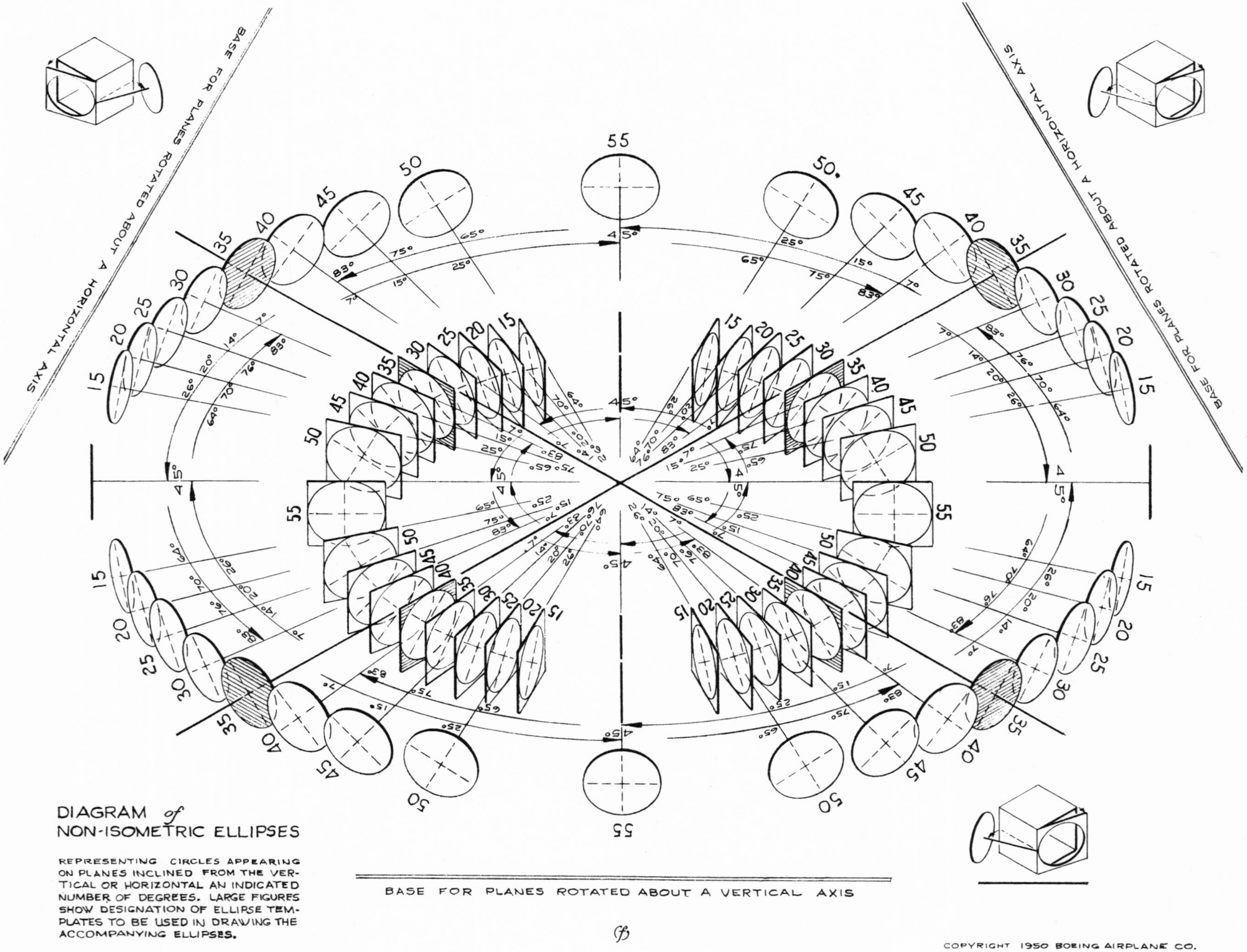

DIAGRAM of NON-ISOMETRIC ELLIPSES
REPRESENTING CIRCLES APPEARING ON PLANES INCLINED FROM THE VERTICAL OR HORIZONTAL AN INDICATED NUMBER OF DEGREES. LARGE FIGURES SHOW DESIGNATION OF ELLIPSE TEMPLATES TO BE USED IN DRAWING THE ACCOMPANYING ELLIPSES.
BASE FOR PLANES ROTATED ABOUT A HORIZONTAL AXIS
BASE FOR PLANES ROTATED ABOUT A HORIZONTAL AXIS
BASE FOR PLANES ROTATED ABOUT A VERTICAL AXIS
COPYRIGHT 1950 BOEING AIRPLANE CO.

Fig. 4-13 Nonisometric ellipse diagram. (Boeing Airplane Co.)

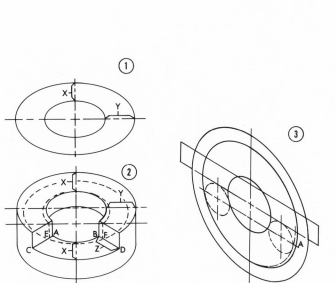

Fig. 4-14 Ellipse oddities.

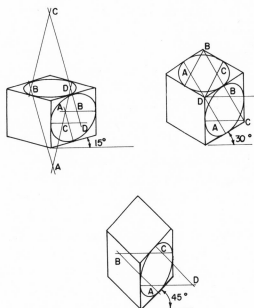

Fig. 4-15 Plotting ellipses.

Drawing Ellipse When Major and Minor Axes Are Known. A simple way to draw an ellipse when the minor and major axes are known is shown in Fig. 4-16. The following procedure is used:

1. Draw a line *AB* equal to major axis.
2. At the center of line *AB* draw line *CD* perpendicular to *AB* and equal to the minor axis.
3. From point *C* draw 15° angle *X*.
4. From point *A* draw 60° angle *Y*.
5. Through point *E* draw 60° line *EG*.
6. With *F* as center and *AF* as radius draw arc as shown.
7. With *G* as center and *CG* as radius, draw arc as shown.
8. Locate point *H* same as *F* and draw arc.

9. Locate *I* same as *G* and draw arc completing the ellipse.

The use of the ellipse template for drawing holes, spheres, and irregular shapes is discussed in Chap. 5, on basic techniques.

Mathematical Ellipse Principles. The distance across the minor axis of an angle ellipse can be found by multiplying the sine of the angle by the diameter of the ellipse desired. The sine of an angle can be found in a trigonometric table.

The distance across the minor axis of an isometric ellipse is 0.706 times the diameter of the ellipse. This is determined by taking the sine of 35° 16′, which is 0.577, and multiplying it by 1.22474, since isometric is 1.22474 (1¼) times larger than a true representation. The distance across the major axis of an isometric ellipse is 1¼ times the indicated diameter.

To find the minor-axis distance of a 1-in. 30° ellipse, multiply the sine of 30°, which is 0.500, by 1, and the result is, of course, ½ in. This is one example of finding the minor axis for angle ellipses, and all the other angle ellipses can be calculated by using the sines of the angles in the same manner.

The major-axis distance of all angle ellipses is equal to the diameter indicated. Some ellipse templates,

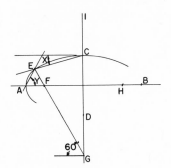

Fig. 4-16 Drawing ellipse when major and minor axes are known.

however, allow an extra 0.020 to 0.022 in. for the pencil or pen.

When the major and minor axes for ellipses are known, they can be plotted by using the method shown in Fig. 4-16.

Use of the 35° Ellipse for Isometric. The 35° ellipse template can be used as an isometric ellipse, providing the desired diameter is multiplied by $1\frac{1}{4}$. This multiplication is necessary because isometric drawings are $1\frac{1}{4}$ times larger than true representations. For example, if a $1''$ isometric ellipse is desired, the $1\frac{1}{4}$ 35° ellipse should be used.

Isometric Ellipse as a 35° Ellipse. Since the 35° ellipse template can be used as an isometric ellipse, it follows that the isometric can be used as a 35° template. The procedure would be just the opposite, however. If a 1-in. 35° ellipse were desired, the $\frac{13}{16}$-in. isometric ellipse would be used. In other words, multiply the $1''$ by 0.816 (1 in. divided by 1.22474 or $1\frac{1}{4}$) to get the proper size to use for the 35° angle ellipse.

When using the angle ellipses on nonisometric planes, be sure to multiply the diameter desired by $1\frac{1}{4}$ as explained in Chap. 3.

Omicron Ellipsograph. A special instrument for drawing ellipses is shown in Fig. 4-18. Any angle-size ellipse can be drawn by setting the major- and minor-axis distances on the sliding arm.

THE HEXAGON TEMPLATE

The procedure for using the hexagon template is similar to the one for using the ellipse template. Although the hexagon template is probably not used

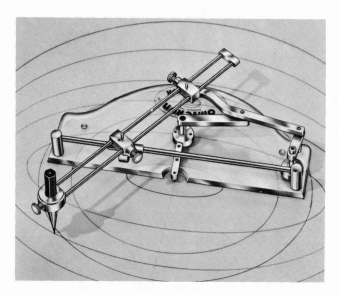

Fig. 4-18 Ellipse machine. (Fullerton Engineering)

as often as the ellipse template, knowing how to use it properly is no less important.

The hexagon template is used to make all types of hex nuts, bolts, shafts, and hexagon holes. The two important parts of the hexagon, as learned in orthographic drawing, are the distance across the corners and the distance across the flats. The distance across the flats is shown by A in Fig. 4-19. This is the distance from the flat surface on one side through the center to the flat on the opposite side. The distance across the corners is shown by B in Fig. 4-19. This is the distance from one corner of the hexagon through the center to a corner on the opposite side.

The angles shown on the Hexangle template (Fig. 4-24) are the same as the angles shown on angle ellipse templates; that is, the angle is the angle between the horizontal line of sight and the plane of the surface. Some manufacturers, however, designate the angles by using the complement of the angle of projection: the 15° angle is shown as 75°, the 60°

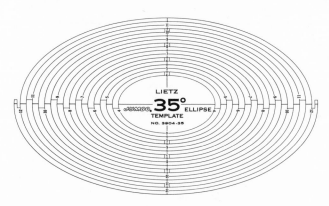

Fig. 4-17 Jumbo ellipse. (The Lietz Co.)

Fig. 4-19 Hexagon distance across flats and corners.

angle as 30° in the same way that some manufacturers designate angle sizes on ellipses.

The minor axis of the hex (Fig. 4-20), or the shortest distance across the flats, is always aligned with the axis of the bolt or hole in the same way that the ellipse is aligned, not as shown in Fig. 4-21.

Position of the Hex Nut. The proper position of a hex nut and bolt head on a three-dimensional drawing is shown in Fig. 4-22. Notice that the minor axis of the hex is aligned with the axis of the bolt or hole. Figure 4-23 shows the incorrect way to use the hex and the distortion that results.

Use of the Hexangle Template. The Hexangle template (Fig. 4-24) by Rapidesign, Inc. has angle sizes for 15, 30, 45, 60, and 90°. A step-by-step

MINOR AXIS

Fig. 4-20 Hexagon showing minor axis.

Fig. 4-21 Hexagon showing flats in incorrect position.

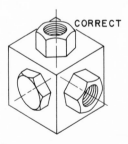

CORRECT

Fig. 4-22 Correct drawing of hexagon.

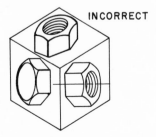

INCORRECT

Fig. 4-23 Incorrect drawing of hexagon.

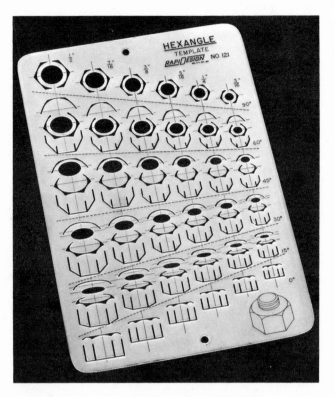

Fig. 4-24 Hexangle template. (Rapidesign, Inc.)

illustration for the use of this template is given in Fig. 4-25. The Hexangle template is used on nonisometric, dimetric, trimetric, perspective, and oblique illustrations. This template is not used for isometric planes. There is a special hexagon template for isometric planes.

When using the hexangle template on nonisometric planes, be sure to multiply the diameter size desired by $1\frac{1}{4}$ for the same reason that angle ellipse templates must be multiplied by $1\frac{1}{4}$ when used on nonisometric planes. (See Fig. 3-13.)

Use of the Isometric Hexagon Template. The isometric hexagon template (Fig. 4-26) is used for isometric planes. A step-by-step illustration demonstrating the use of the isometric hexagon template by Rapidesign is shown in Fig. 4-27.

The size shown on this template is the distance across the flats of the hexagon. Because of this you must multiply the size of the bolt by $1\frac{1}{2}$ to determine the proper hex to use, since the distance across the flats of a hex is about $1\frac{1}{2}$ times the body of the bolt. The thickness of the head of a nominal bolt is $\frac{2}{3}$ of the diameter of the bolt or distance B. This distance

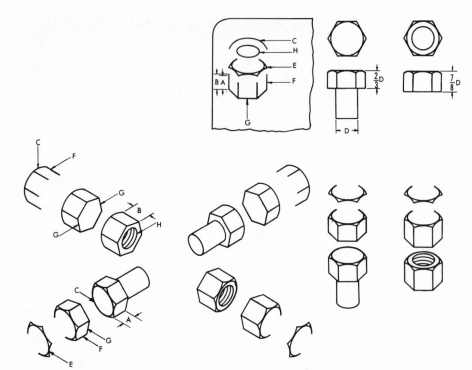

Fig. 4-25 Use of Hexangle template.

is not indicated on the template and will have to be computed. The thickness of the nut is about $7/8$ of the diameter of the bolt or distance A, which is indicated on the template.

The hexagon shape at F is obtained by drawing half of the hexagon and then turning the template over to draw the other half. The threads are drawn with the proper-size isometric ellipse.

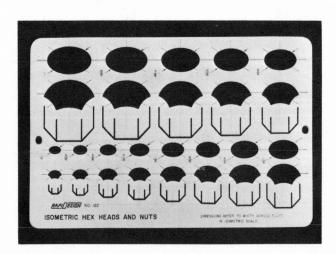

Fig. 4-26 Isometric hexagon template.

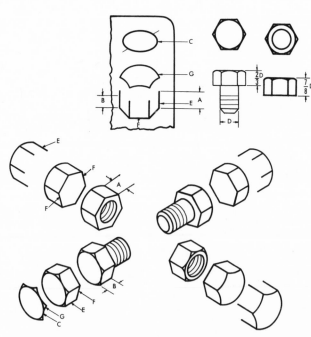

Fig. 4-27 Use of isometric hexagon template.

Questions

1. What is the main use of the ellipse template?
2. What is the major axis?   Minor axis?
3. Name two types of ellipse templates.
4. What is the main difference between these two templates?
5. What is the most important fact to remember when using the ellipse template?
6. What determines the proper angle-size ellipse?
7. How can you determine the minor axis of an ellipse?
8. Describe a method for plotting an ellipse.
9. How can you draw an ellipse when the major and minor axes are known?
10. Name two important parts of a hexagon.
11. Describe a method for plotting a hexagon.

Exercises

Refer to Chap. 3 and select problems that require the ellipse template to draw holes, fillets, rounds, and partial arcs of a circle.   Make isometric drawings of these problems.   Do not draw problems with holes on inclined planes.   Draw only those with holes on horizontal or vertical surfaces.   Use only the isometric ellipse template for these horizontal or vertical planes.

Be sure the minor axis of the isometric ellipse is aligned with the axis of the hole or arc.   Study the drawings for fillets and rounds in Chap. 5 (Problems: Group 2).

See Chap. 8 for hexagon bolt and nut problems. Make isometric views of hexagons using the isometric hexagon template.

5 BASIC TECHNIQUES, INTERSECTIONS, AND SECTIONS

This chapter presents many basic techniques and procedures used in technical illustration. These are practical methods for drawing various shapes and irregular objects involving ellipses, spheres, circles, angles, and hexagons.

Also included in this chapter are techniques for constructing intersections and sections, fillets, rounds, chamfers, holes, and the torus. Aircraft reference planes are also illustrated and discussed.

THE SPHERE

The construction of a sphere or parts of a sphere is a technique often needed in technical illustration. A sphere is a true circle in three-dimensional drawing. If only a complete sphere is desired, the illustrator needs simply to draw a circle equal in diameter to the diameter of the sphere. When drawing an isometric sphere, however, draw the circle $1\frac{1}{4}$ times larger than the diameter of the desired sphere, because isometric drawings are $1\frac{1}{4}$ times larger than true representations, as discussed in Chap. 3. This is shown in Fig. 5-1, which illustrates the drawing of an isometric sphere using isometric ellipse templates. One isometric ellipse is drawn with the

minor axis aligned with axis *AB*, and the other is drawn perpendicular to axis *AB* with the minor axis aligned with axis *CD*.

Half of a sphere is shown in Fig. 5-2, and three-fourths of a sphere is indicated in Fig. 5-3. In Fig. 5-4 less than one-fourth of the sphere is cutaway, and

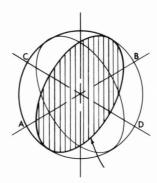

Fig. 5-2 Drawing half isometric sphere.

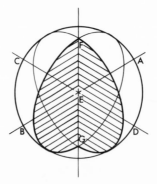

Fig. 5-3 Drawing three-fourths isometric sphere.

Fig. 5-1 Drawing isometric sphere.

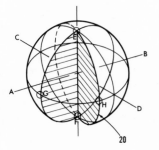

Fig. 5-4 Locating points on sphere.

points *G* and *H* are on the outside of the sphere. In order to locate points on the outside surface of a sphere, the proper diameter-size ellipse must pass through the axis of rotation points *E* and *F* and the given points, in this case, *G* and *H*. The 20° ellipse passes through points *E*, *H*, and *F*, while the isometric ellipse passes through points *E*, *G*, and *F*. Line *AB* is the minor-axis line for the 20° ellipse, and line *CD* is the minor-axis line for the isometric ellipse.

Sphere Method for Finding Angle-size Ellipse.

The sphere is a useful device for finding the proper angle-size ellipse for off-axis planes. Figures 5-5 to 5-8c give examples of practical problems using the sphere to solve angle-size ellipses.

In Fig. 5-5 the crosshatched inclined plane has been rotated forward 16° from the vertical with line *AB* as the axis of rotation. To determine the angle-size ellipse for this inclined plane, select an ellipse that will pass through points *A* and *B* when the minor axis of the ellipse is aligned with line *CD*. This is necessary because line *CD* represents a line perpendicular to line *XY*, the 16° line. The proper angle-size ellipse will actually pass through four points, *X*, *Y*, *A*, and *B*, although only the points *A* and *B* are needed.

Points *A* and *B*, which are on the outside of the

sphere and along the axis of rotation, and line *CD*, which is perpendicular to the plane, are all that are required to determine the angle-size ellipse. The diameter of the angle-size ellipse is, of course, equal to the diameter of the sphere. These are isometric drawings; therefore, the diameter of the angle-size ellipse must be $1\frac{1}{4}$ times the indicated diameter of the sphere. The 20° ellipse is the proper angle size for Fig. 5-5.

This method can be used in dimetric and trimetric drawings by simply substituting the proper angle-size ellipses for the isometric. Measure the angles by plotting as shown in Fig. 5-22. In isometric drawings the Lietz isometric ellipse protractor can be used. (See Chap. 6.)

In some cases no angle-size ellipse will pass exactly through the points *A* and *B*. When this is the case, use the angle size that is nearest to passing through the points, since this accuracy is entirely satisfactory. (See Fig. 5-5a.)

Figure 5-6 shows another vertical-plane rotation tilted 16° back from the vertical, and in this instance the 45° ellipse is found to be the angle size that passes through points *A* and *B*. Figures 5-7 and 5-8 show the axis of rotation *AB* along the vertical line with the points *X* and *Y* rotated in the horizontal plane.

In actual practice, when solving these problems, only one isometric ellipse is needed in the vertical plane for vertical-plane rotations. For horizontal rotations, two isometric ellipses are needed, one in the vertical plane and one in the horizontal plane. Use at least a 2-in. isometric ellipse in order to obtain satisfactory accuracy. Practical application of sphere-method techniques is shown in Figs. 5-5a–5-5c, 5-6a–5-6c, 5-7a–5-7c, and 5-8a–5-8c.

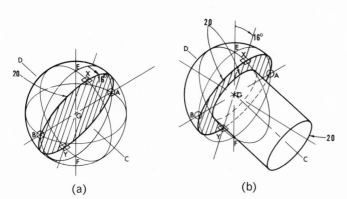

(a)   (b)

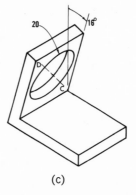

(c)

Fig. 5-5 (a) Sphere method for off-axis ellipse. (b) Sphere-method problem solution. (c) Sphere-method problem solution.

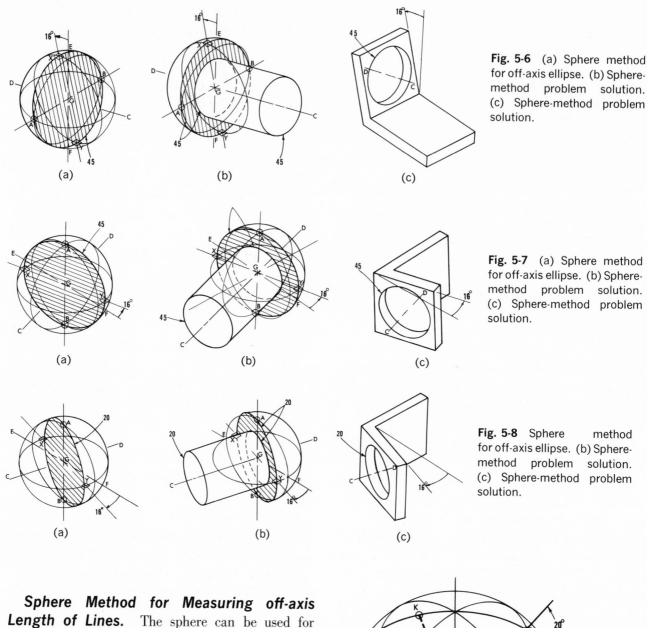

Fig. 5-6 (a) Sphere method for off-axis ellipse. (b) Sphere-method problem solution. (c) Sphere-method problem solution.

Fig. 5-7 (a) Sphere method for off-axis ellipse. (b) Sphere-method problem solution. (c) Sphere-method problem solution.

Fig. 5-8 Sphere method for off-axis ellipse. (b) Sphere-method problem solution. (c) Sphere-method problem solution.

Sphere Method for Measuring off-axis Length of Lines. The sphere can be used for measuring off-axis length of lines as shown in Fig. 5-9. Lines *AB*, *AC*, *AE*, *AF*, *AG*, *AH*, *AJ*, and *AK* all represent equal length but at different angles. They are equal because they represent radii of the sphere.

Line *AB* is along the isometric axis and can be measured. Line *AC* is in a vertical plane 20° from the horizontal. Point *C* is located at the point where the 20° line crosses the isometric ellipse in the vertical plane. To locate the other lines that represent equal lengths, an isometric line is drawn from point *C* to the vertical axis of the sphere, point *D*. With

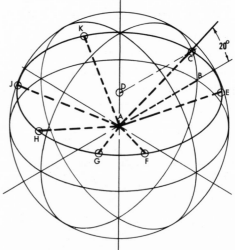

Fig. 5-9 Sphere method of measuring length of lines.

point *D* as center, an isometric ellipse is drawn that will pass through point *C*. In this example points *E*, *F*, *G*, *H*, *J*, and *K* are selected at random along the isometric ellipse in the horizontal plane. These lines are compound-angle lines.

To find the proper ellipse to use when a specific point is desired on the outside surface of the sphere, proceed in the following way: Select the ellipse which will pass through the point and in which the major-axis points of the ellipse will coincide with the major-axis points of the sphere. Figure 5-5 shows one-half of a sphere with points *A*, *X*, *Y*, and *B* located on the outside surface of the sphere. The 20° ellipse was used to find the outside surface of the sphere following the procedure explained above. Figure 5-6 locates points *A*, *X*, *Y*, and *B* on the outside surface by using the 45° ellipse template.

Flat Surface on Sphere. The technique for drawing a flat surface on a sphere is shown in Fig. 5-10. An orthographic view of a sphere is shown with a ½″ flat surface on the top, a ½″ flat surface on the bottom, and a $\frac{7}{16}$″ flat surface on the side. The diameter of the sphere is $\frac{13}{16}$″. To draw an isometric illustration of this sphere, begin by drawing two isometric ellipses $\frac{13}{16}$″ in diameter, one perpen-

dicular to the other as explained in Fig. 5-1. Draw the circle tangent to the major-axis points of the ellipses. The diameter of this circle is actually about 1¼″, but this circle represents the isometric drawing of the $\frac{13}{16}$″ sphere. Draw the ½″ isometric ellipse on the top of the sphere as shown. To draw the flat surface on the side, you must first find the outside point on the sphere. This point is at the intersection of axis *CD* with the ellipse. Measure the distance *Y* along axis *CD* and draw the $\frac{7}{16}$″ isometric ellipse. The flat surface on the bottom of the sphere does not show; however, the procedure is the same for the bottom of the sphere as for the top.

Practical application of sphere techniques is shown in Fig. 5-11. Chapter 9 illustrates many more applications of sphere techniques.

THE COUNTERSUNK HOLE

Ellipse templates are used in drawing a countersunk hole as shown in Fig. 5-12. An orthographic view of a screw or rivet head is also shown. This is an isometric drawing showing countersunk holes. Normally, countersunk holes are drawn as shown on surface *X*. The large ellipse is the size of the diameter of the top of the screw or rivet head. This ellipse

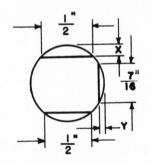

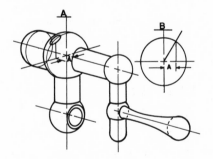

Fig. 5-11 Sphere solutions on problem.

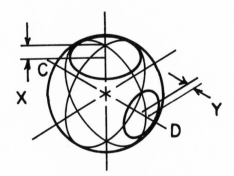

Fig. 5-10 Drawing flat surface on sphere-isometric.

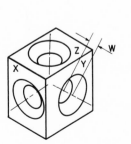

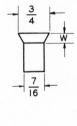

Fig. 5-12 Countersunk hole.

COUNTERSUNK
    HOLE

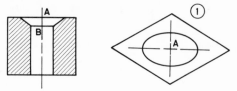
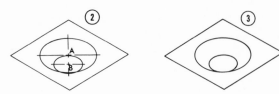

Fig. 5-13 Drawing countersunk hole.

is drawn first. The smaller ellipse, which is the size of the hole, is drawn tangent to the side of the larger ellipse. In some cases the countersunk hole is drawn as shown on surface *Y*. The large ellipse is drawn equal to the diameter of the top of the screw or rivet head. The smaller ellipse, which is equal to the size of the hole, is drawn by locating the center, using distance *W* shown on the orthographic view. This distance is measured along the axis of the hole from the center of the larger ellipse toward the center of the block. With this point as center, draw the small ellipse. Of course, only part of the ellipse will show. The countersunk hole on surface *Z* is drawn by the same procedure as on *Y*. Usually the more simple method is used as shown on surface *X*, since exact accuracy is seldom needed on an illustration for a countersunk hole. A step-by-step illustration with an orthographic section view is shown for a countersunk hole in Fig. 5-13.

THE COUNTERBORED HOLE

The counterbored hole is drawn with ellipse templates as shown in Fig. 5-14. The holes are drawn to the dimensions shown in the orthographic sectional view. First use the $\frac{1}{2}''$ ellipse to draw the large hole on the outside surface. To show the depth of the counterbore, move the $\frac{1}{2}''$ isometric ellipse along the axis toward the center of the block, a distance equal to the depth of the counterbore, and draw the second ellipse. With the same center, draw the $\frac{3}{8}''$ hole with the isometric template. A step-by-step illustration with an orthographic section view is shown for a counterbored hole in Fig. 5-15.

For dimetric, trimetric, and perspective drawings the technique would be the same except that the proper angle-size ellipse would be used instead of the isometric ellipse.

A BEAD-UP OR FLANGED-OUT HOLE

The bead-up hole, sometimes called flanged-out hole, appears frequently in sheet metal. This type of

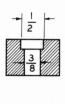

Fig. 5-14 Counterbored hole.

COUNTERBORED
    HOLE

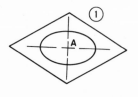
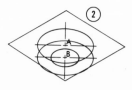
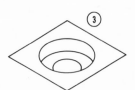

Fig. 5-15 Drawing counterbored hole.

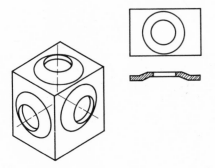

Fig. 5-16 Bead-up or flanged-out hole.

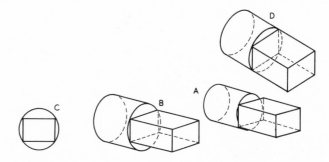

Fig. 5-18 Allowance for minor axis of ellipse.

hole is also drawn with ellipse templates as illustrated in Fig. 5-16. First draw the large ellipse equal to the distance shown in the orthographic view. Draw the small hole with the ellipse tangent to the large ellipse as shown. To show the thickness of the metal, move the small ellipse inward along the axis and draw another small ellipse. A step-by-step illustration is shown for a flanged-out hole in Fig. 5-17.

For dimetric, trimetric, and perspective drawings the technique is the same except that the proper angle-size ellipse would be used instead of the isometric ellipse template.

ALLOWANCE FOR FORESHORTENED MINOR AXIS OF ELLIPSE

A problem sometimes arises when using angle ellipse templates because of the foreshortened distance across the minor axis. An example of one problem is shown in Fig. 5-18.

An orthographic end view of the intersection of a cylinder and rectangular shape appears in view C. If this object is drawn according to the orthographic view, we obtain a drawing like view A, which shows the rectangular shape extending beyond the cylinder. This is a dimetric drawing which requires the use of an angle ellipse. So that the proper picture will be

shown, the cylinder must be enlarged or the rectangular shape reduced in size, allowing the corners to coincide with the ellipse. Normally the cylinder is enlarged (view B).

Similar problems will arise when an angle ellipse is involved, as the minor axis of an angle ellipse is always less than the actual diameter of the circle it represents, and concentric ellipses are not actually concentric. Other examples are shown in Chap. 9. An isometric drawing of this problem, view D, shows a picture that is satisfactory because the isometric ellipse is true distance across the 30° axis of the ellipse.

IRREGULAR HYDRAULIC LINES AND WIRES

The drawing of irregular hose lines, hydraulic lines, rods, wires, and bundles of wires (Fig. 5-19) can be easily accomplished. First draw a center line in the proper position. Select any ellipse with a major axis equal to the diameter of the object. Draw a number of ellipses along this center line. Using an irregular curve, draw lines tangent to the ellipses at the major-axis points as shown in Fig. 5-19. The outer webbing may be suggested for a bundle of wires as shown in Fig. 5-20. The curved lines can be drawn freehand.

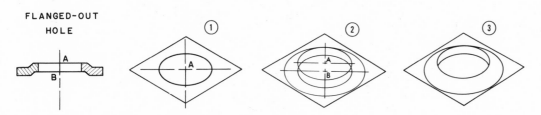

Fig. 5-17 Drawing bead-up or flanged-out hole.

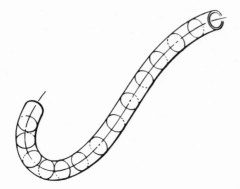

Fig. 5-19 Hoses, hydraulic lines, and wires.

Fig. 5-20 Drawing webbing on wire bundles.

IRREGULAR CURVED SURFACES

An irregular curved object is shown in Fig. 5-21. View *A* shows an orthographic front view and view *B* shows an orthographic side view. These views are partially boxed in, and random points are established. These points are then located on the axis of the illustration using a coordinate-points procedure.

PLOTTING ANGLES

Plotting angles can easily be accomplished by using a coordinate-point system as shown in Fig. 5-22. A front and side orthographic view of an object is shown

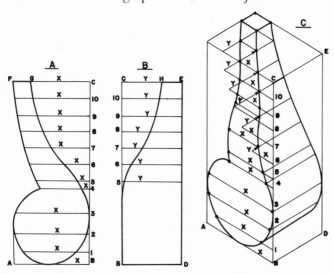

Fig. 5-21 Drawing irregular-curved objects.

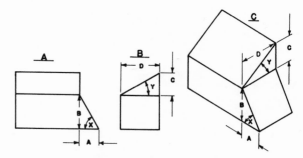

Fig. 5-22 Plotting angles.

in views *A* and *B*. Plot the angles as shown in view *C* by locating distances *A*, *B*, *C*, and *D*.

ROUNDED EDGES

Rounded edges on surfaces are shown in several ways, as in Fig. 5-23. The lines along the edges in views *B*, *C*, and *E* are only suggested. In view *A*, the solid line is shown with the three arcs drawn at the corners. When only one edge is rounded, no line is shown in most cases, because the contour is shown by the arcs on the sharp edges (view *D*).

BREAKS FOR CUTAWAY SECTIONS

A flat metal cutaway section is shown in Fig. 5-24. Care should be taken in drawing the sharp points. Distances *A*, *B*, and *C* should be equal; otherwise the point will appear to be bent. Cutaway sections are shown for round shafts or pipe in Fig. 5-25. Both methods are used, although view *B* is probably used more often.

DRAWING STRAP AT INTERSECTION OF PIPES

The front and side orthographic views and the completed illustration of a pipe intersection with a

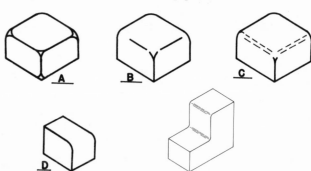

Fig. 5-23 Drawing rounded edges.

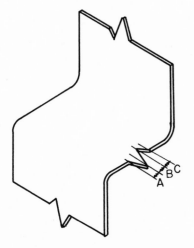

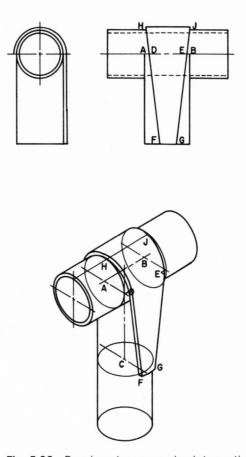

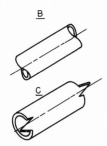

Fig. 5-24   Drawing cutaway sections.

Fig. 5-25   Drawing cutaway sections of pipe.

Fig. 5-26   Drawing strap over pipe intersection.

strap are shown in Fig. 5-26.   To draw the illustration, proceed as follows:

1. Locate points *A* and *B* and draw ellipses.
2. Draw an ellipse at point *C* to locate outer surface
    of vertical pipe.
3. Find points *D*, *E*, *F*, and *G*.
4. Draw arc *HD* and *JE*.
5. Draw lines *DF* and *EG*.
6. Add thickness of strap.
7. Draw lines tangent to ellipses to complete
    horizontal pipe, and draw vertical lines tangent
    to ellipses to complete vertical pipe.

INTERSECTIONS

An intersection of two cylinders is shown in Fig.
5-27.   As shown in Fig. 5-27, view *A*, draw two
center lines perpendicular to each other for the axis
of the two cylinders.   Draw the ellipses equal to the
size of the cylinders.   Select points along the vertical
center line of one of the cylinders.   It is probably

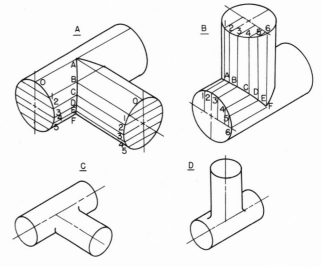

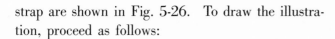

Fig. 5-27   Drawing intersection of pipes.

better to lay off equal distances.   Measure the same
distances along vertical center line of the other
cylinder.   Draw lines from the points on the vertical

center lines of cylinders to the outer edge of the cylinders. From these points draw lines parallel to the cylinders until they intersect at *A*, *B*, *C*, *D*, *E*, and *F*. Connect these points with an irregular curve to make the proper line of intersection. Follow the same procedure for view *B* but divide the horizontal center lines of the cylinders into equal points.

Often, because of the small size of some cylinders, a simplified method is used which is satisfactory for small intersections, as shown in views *C* and *D*. A step-by-step procedure is shown in Fig. 5-28 for drawing an intersection of two cylindrical parts at 90°. Figure 5-29*a* shows the technique for drawing an intersection at less than 90°.

The off-center intersection of two cylindrical parts of different diameter is illustrated in Fig. 5-29*b*. The top and front orthographic views and the three steps for the solution using isometric drawing are shown. Several random points on the orthographic views are selected and transferred to the illustration. Points from the top view, shown by lines *JK*, *GH*, and *EF*, are measured in step 2 by simply measuring along

the axes. Other points may be selected, such as shown by the other lines; however, the three shown are adequate to solve this intersection. Connect points *H*, *K*, and *F*, and the result is shown in step 3.

Figure 5-30 shows another intersection of a hole on a cylindrical surface. Steps 1, 2, and 3 illustrate the isometric solution. The angle 20° is measured, and a partial ellipse is drawn locating point *C′* on the outside surface of the cylinder. An isometric ellipse equal to the diameter of the round hole is drawn with the axes *PQ* and *RS* at a convenient distance from the object. Axis *RS* is along the 30° isometric axis. The points *P*, *S*, *Q*, and *R* are then projected parallel to axis *A′C′*. At the surface of the object they locate *P′*, *S′*, *Q′*, and *R′*. Connect these points with a curve, and the result is the egg shape in step 3. Be sure that the plotted hole does not extend beyond the lines *R′R* and *S′S*. Other typical intersections, like the one in Fig. 5-30, appear in Figs. 5-31 and 5-32. The procedure for solving these problems is practically the same.

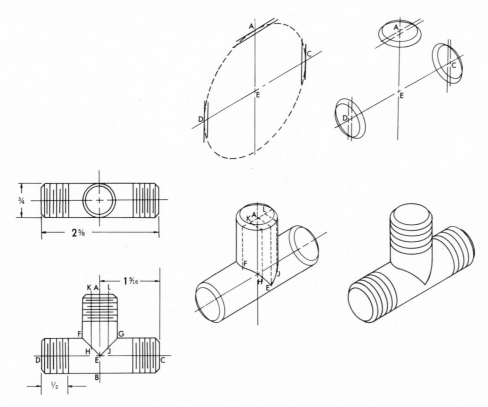

Fig. 5-28 Drawing pipe intersection.

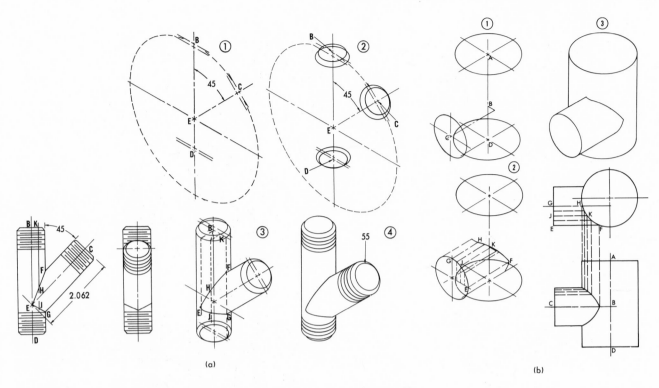

Fig. 5-29 (a) Drawing pipe intersection. (b) Drawing off-center intersection.

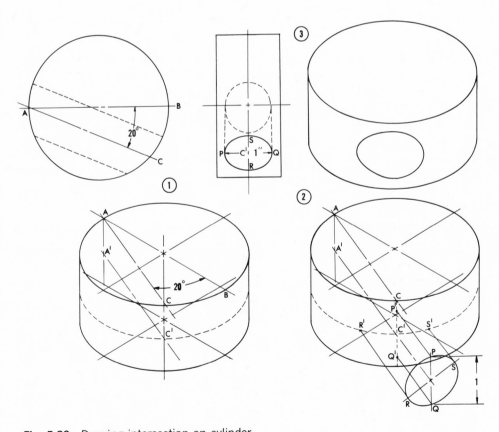

Fig. 5-30 Drawing intersection on cylinder.

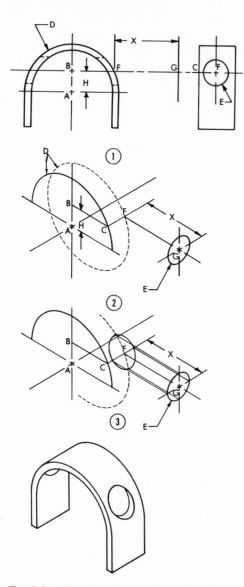

Fig. 5-31 Drawing hole on curved surface.

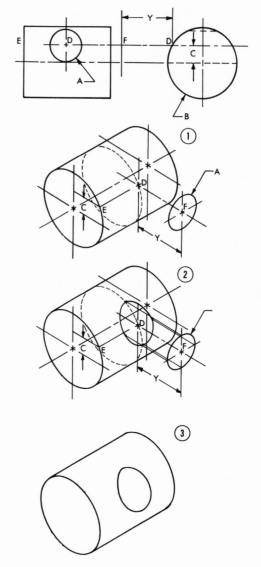

Fig. 5-32 Drawing hole off-center.

Figure 5-33 shows methods for drawing a hole on a cylindrical object intersecting at 90° and at the center. The large dashed ellipse locates the outside surface of the horizontal cylinder. An ellipse equal in diameter to the size of the hole is centered at point D, a convenient distance from the object. Random points, such as K, D, and N, are then established along axis GH. The points are projected vertically to the large dashed ellipse locating points V, C, and W. Lines YZ, QR, and ST are drawn with indefinite length, and points J, E, M, L, F, G, H, and O are projected vertically to locate points Y, Q, S, Z, R, U, X, and T. Connect these points with a curve for

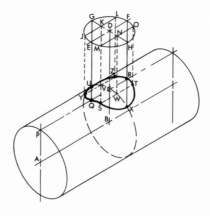

Fig. 5-33 Drawing hole on cylinder.

the completed intersection and shape of the round isometric hole.

SECTIONS

The same practices used in orthographic drawing apply to sections in technical illustration. The cutting planes of half and full sections should be placed along the axes of the illustration, as shown in Fig. 5-34. Cross-hatching is made in much the same way in sections as in orthographic. On a vertical surface the cross-hatching is drawn at an opposite angle to the cross-hatching on the horizontal surface, as illustrated in the half sections. This aids in visualizing the two different planes.

Broken-out sections (Fig. 5-35) are sometimes used to show otherwise hidden parts or shapes. Make a zigzag line to show the cutaway.

A complete exploded section illustration is shown in Fig. 5-44.

LOCATING HOLES ON CYLINDRICAL SURFACES

The important point to keep in mind when locating holes on cylindrical surfaces is the position of the horizontal and vertical axes of the cylinders. Figure 5-36 shows the proper method for projecting the axes

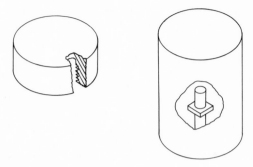

Fig. 5-35   Broken-out sections.

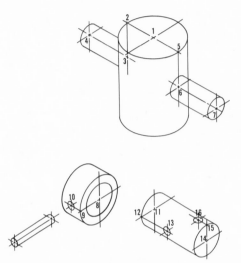

Fig. 5-36   Locating hole on cylinder.

of the ellipses to locate the holes. There is no need to plot the ellipses at points 6, 10, 13, or 16 unless the holes are much larger, as shown in Fig. 5-33.

ROUND, CHAMFER, RECESSED, AND SPHERICAL SHAPES

Top and front orthographic views are shown (Fig. 5-37) with the step-by-step solution for these varied shapes. When there is no hole in objects A and B, place a small arc along one of the horizontal axes of the illustration. The arc helps to identify the curved surface.

TORUS AND FLAT WASHER

Step-by-step illustrations showing variations in the construction of torus and flat washer are shown in Figs. 5-38 to 5-40 (pages 60 to 61) with the orthographic front and side views and the isometric solutions.

By deleting the upper part of ellipse C and the

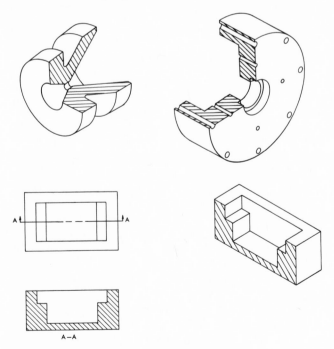

Fig. 5-34   Half section and full section.

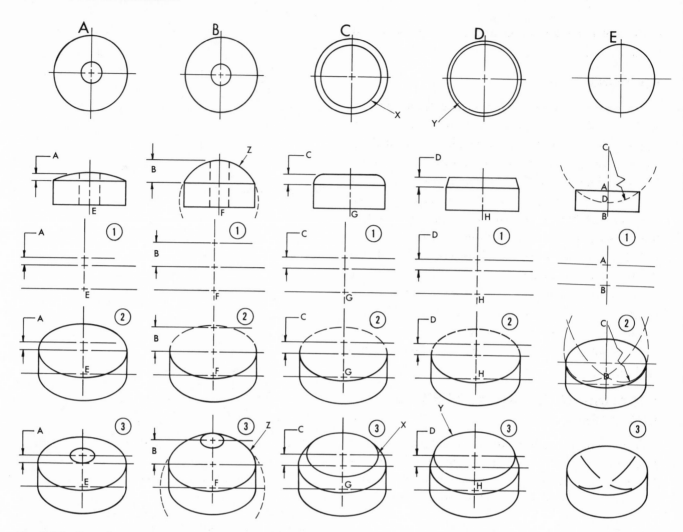

Fig. 5-37 Round, crown, chamfer, depression, and curved end.

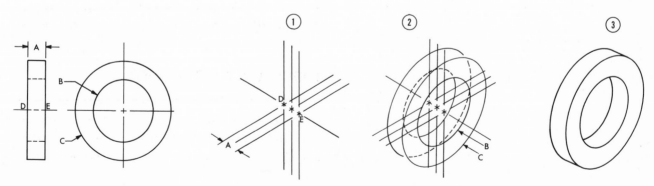

Fig. 5-38 Drawing washer.

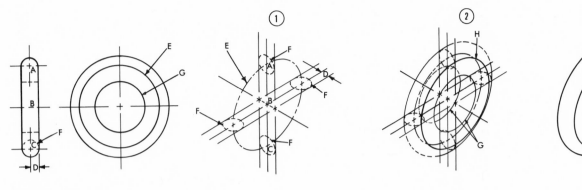

Fig. 5-39 Drawing torus.

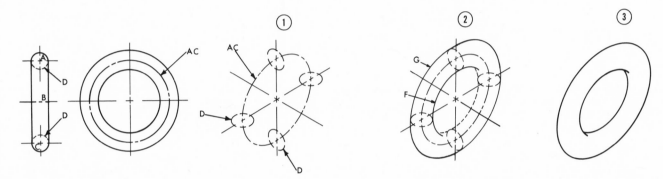

Fig. 5-40 Drawing torus.

lower part of ellipse *B* (Fig. 5-38, step 2 of the washer), you can obtain a reasonably accurate representation of a torus. It is important that you accurately show the short runouts, as illustrated in step 3 of the torus (Fig. 5-40).

Sometimes it is permissible to make the exterior of the torus with a complete large ellipse at *G* (step 2 of Fig. 5-40) and the inner lines with the proper diameter 30° ellipse. The two short runouts may then be added.

To make dimetric, trimetric, or perspective illustrations of the torus and flat washer, employ the same procedure but use the proper angle-size ellipse for the planes instead of the isometric ellipse. See the chapter on dimetric and trimetric to determine the proper angle-size ellipse to use.

FILLETS, ROUNDS, RUNOUTS, AND KNURLING

A number of examples are shown for making fillets, rounds, runouts, and knurling in Fig. 5-41. Use of the ellipse with fillets and rounds is shown in Fig.

5-42. The example of a fillet shown at point *C* in Fig. 5-41 is seldom used. In some cases solid lines are used for the fillets in example *A*, Fig. 5-41. A dashed ellipse is used at *D*, *E*, and *F* to locate the position of the fillet or runout. Do not make the curve too long on the runouts. The knurling indicated at *G* in Fig. 5-41 is drawn with straight lines and rarely with a curved line.

AIRCRAFT REFERENCE PLANES

In the aircraft industry, reference planes are used to locate specific points on the aircraft, and sometimes these reference planes are used for dimensioning on blueprints. An illustration of these reference planes is shown in Fig. 5-43.

The fuselage reference line *FRL* is the base line for vertical and horizontal measurements. Fuselage station *FUS STA* is horizontal distance shown in inches, starting at the nose of the aircraft and progressing toward the tail. Station zero is usually at the tip of the nose; however, it may be ahead of the nose or behind it because of design changes. If

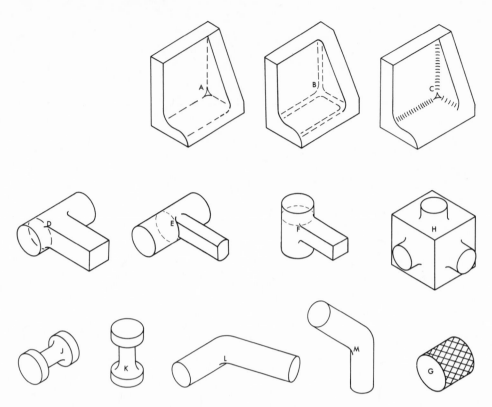

Fig. 5-41 Fillets, rounds, runouts, and knurling.

station zero is behind the tip of the nose, the stations in front of the nose will be negative numbers.

Water line *WL* is vertical distance, starting at the fuselage reference line and extending upward or downward. The distance below the fuselage refer-

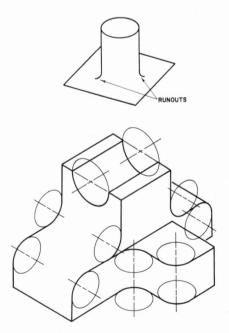

Fig. 5-42 Drawing fillets and rounds using ellipse.

ence line is shown as a minus number; the distance above is assumed as a plus number. No plus sign is used, however. Both distances are expressed in inches. Some companies use a base line for water-line measurements at a point below the aircraft, thereby eliminating the minus numbers.

Buttock line *BL* is horizontal distance from the fuselage reference line to the outside of the fuselage, both right and left. It is expressed in inches. Some companies use a wing Butt Line.

Wing station *W STA* is the horizontal distance shown in inches, starting at the fuselage reference line and extending toward the tip of the wings.

Wing station zero is usually at the center line of the fuselage, although in some aircraft it is at the outside of the fuselage.

Questions

1. What is the shape of a sphere in three-dimensional drawing?
2. How does the size of a sphere drawn with the isometric ellipse template compare with a sphere drawn with the angle ellipse template? Explain.

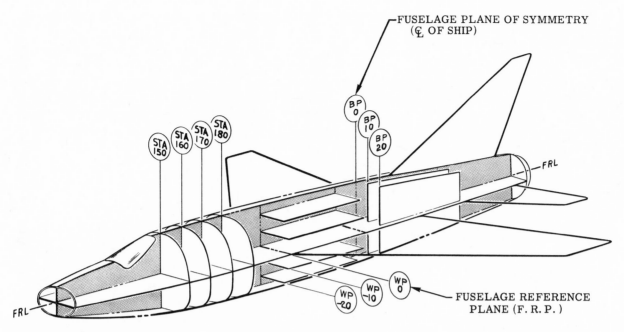

Fig. 5-43 Aircraft reference planes. (North American Aviation, Inc.)

3. Describe the method for finding a point on the outside surface of a sphere.

4. Draw a sphere showing one-eighth of the area cut away.

5. What problem appears when drawing a view of a cylinder which has a rectangular-shaped end?

6. Draw an illustration of a rubber tire, using methods shown in this chapter.

7. Draw an illustration of a tapered shaft with a diameter of 1″ at one end and ½″ at the other end.

8. What method of construction is used for drawing irregular-shaped objects?

9. Explain how angles are drawn without the aid of a protractor.

10. Show how a break would be shown on a solid, round shaft.

11. Draw an illustration of a 1″ pipe intersecting another 1″ pipe at an angle of 30°.

12. Define the following aircraft terms: fuselage station, water line, buttock line.

Exercises

SPHERES

Draw an isometric view of the vise handle from the vise assembly in the back of the book. Make the drawing double size.

Draw an isometric view of the spherical knob from the trailer hitch assembly in the back of the book.

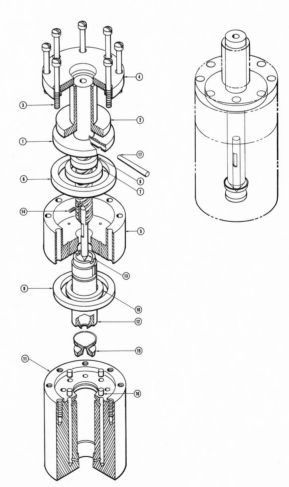

Fig. 5-44 Section illustration.

PROBLEMS: GROUP 2

Fillets, Rounds, Runouts, Chamfers, Washers, and the Boss

Draw these problems in isometric, using the isometric ellipse template.   Be sure the ellipse is aligned properly.

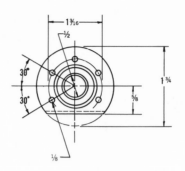

Prob. 2-7   Line fitting.

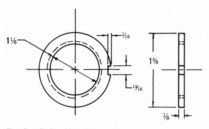

Prob. 2-1   Washer.

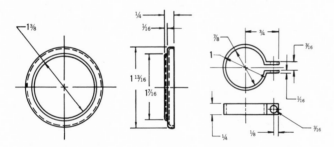

Prob. 2-2   Spacer.

Prob. 2-3   Clamp.

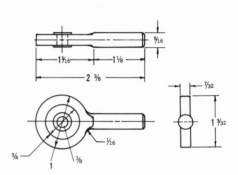

Prob. 2-8   Bearing post.

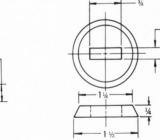

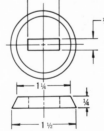

Prob. 2-5   Hose clip.

Prob. 2-4   Slotted washer.

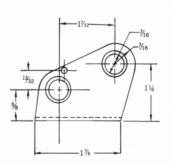

Prob. 2-9   Clevis base.

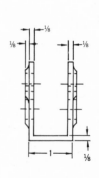

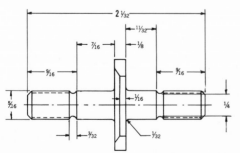

Prob. 2-6   Shaft.

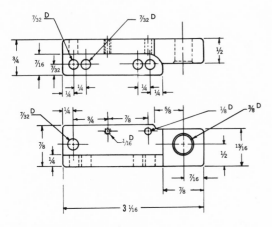

Prob. 2-10   Fixture base.

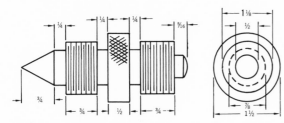

Prob. 2-12   Center pin.

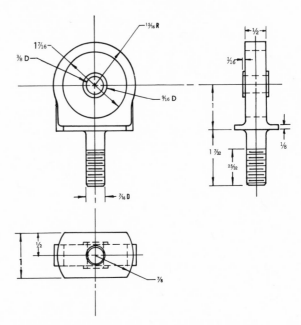

Prob. 2-11   Bearing holder.

PROBLEMS: GROUP 3
Sections and Intersections

Select problems from Group 3 and draw isometric views with full and half sections. Place the cutting-plane lines along the isometric axis, and draw the proper cross-hatching as explained in the chapter.

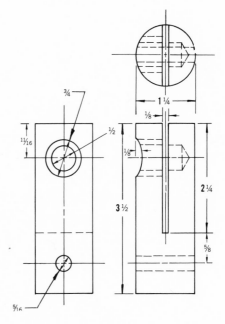

Prob. 3-1   Expansion post.

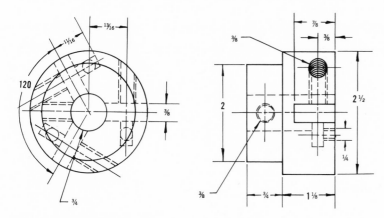

Prob. 3-2   Tripod base.

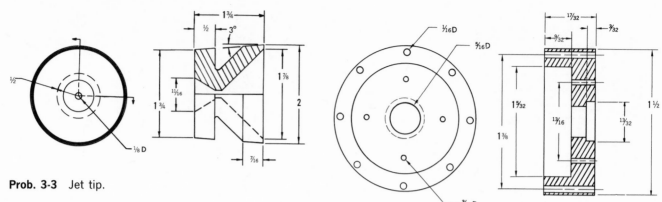

Prob. 3-3   Jet tip.

Prob. 3-4   Plate end.

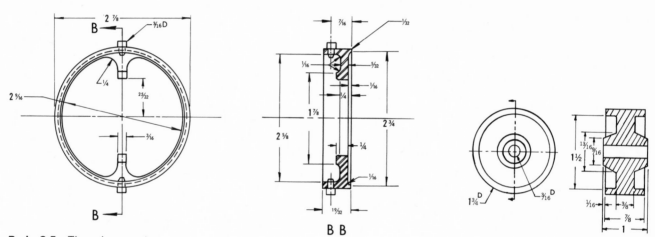

Prob. 3-5   Thread support.

B B

Prob. 3-6   Pulley wheel.

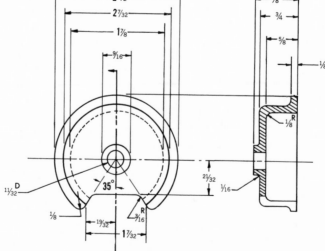

Prob. 3-7   Bearing plate.

PROBLEMS: GROUP 4
The Clevis, Lugs, and Wheels

Draw these problems in isometric, using the iso-metric ellipse template. Draw the compound-curve problem, utilizing the boxing-in procedure.

Draw a torus-tire, tube, or round handwheel, using techniques shown in the chapter.

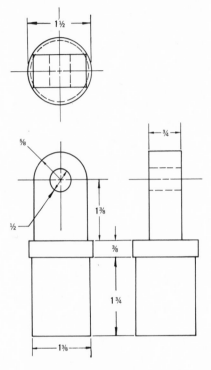

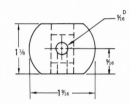

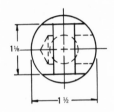

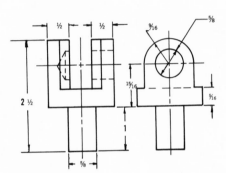

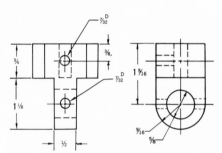

Prob. 4-1 Fork post.

Prob. 4-2 T lug.

Prob. 4-3 Lug post.

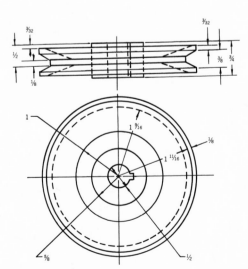

Prob. 4-4 Pulley wheel.

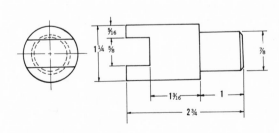

Prob. 4-5 Fork rod.

6 ISOMETRIC ELLIPSE PROTRACTOR

The Lietz isometric ellipse protractor is a versatile instrument that measures simple and compound isometric angles and shows the proper angle-size ellipse to use on nonisometric planes for both simple and compound angles.

This instrument is composed of three parts. (See Fig. 6-1) The numbers along the outer part of the ellipse indicate angles along horizontal and vertical planes. The inner ellipses with the ellipse size indicated show the proper angle-size ellipse to use on simple nonisometric inclined planes. The numbers along the horizontal scale indicate the proper angle-size ellipse to use for oblique nonisometric planes involving compound angles.

This instrument, in the form of a 6-in. isometric ellipse, is widely used and saves valuable time in technical illustration. The protractor can be obtained from The Leitz Co., 1224 S. Hope Street, Los Angeles, California.

MEASURING ANGLES

When measuring isometric angles, always align the minor axis of the ellipse protractor with the axis of rotation, and place the center at the vertex of the angle. The minor axis of the protractor is always aligned with the vertical axis or with one of the 30° horizontal axes except when measuring the ellipse angle size for a compound angle. The minor axis of the protractor is placed perpendicular to the plane of the angle, as illustrated in Fig. 6-2.

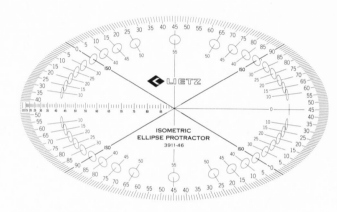

Fig. 6-1 Isometric Ellipse Protractor. (The Lietz Co.)

Finding the Angle-size Ellipse for Nonisometric Planes. To find the proper angle-size ellipse to use on nonisometric surfaces, place the protractor in the same position just described. The angle-size ellipse can be read when the angle is measured, without moving the instrument. (See Fig. 6-2.)

The first step is to locate the line that is perpendicular to the nonisometric surface, since the holes are perpendicular to this surface. When the angle-size ellipse is found, the minor axis of this ellipse must be aligned with the axis of the hole, as explained in Chap. 3. The proper angle-size ellipse to use on the nonisometric surface is indicated where the line perpendicular to the surface crosses the protractor. For example, in Fig. 6-2, view 1, the inclined plane is 25° from the vertical, and the 90° line from the inclined plane crosses the protractor where the 50°

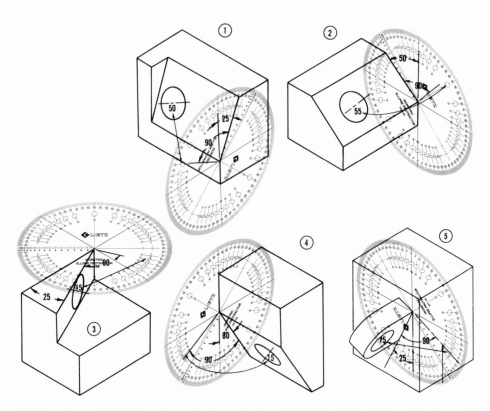

Fig. 6-2 Isometric ellipse protractor solutions.

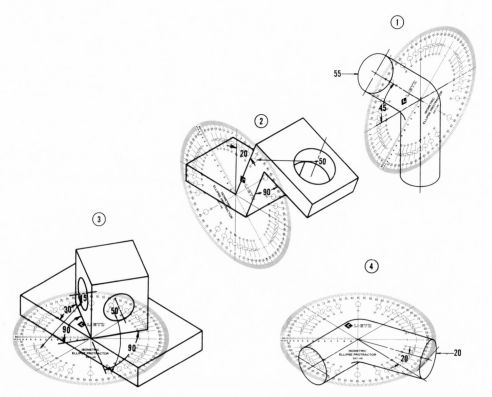

Fig. 6-3 Isometric ellipse protractor solutions.

ellipse is shown. The 50° ellipse would be the correct ellipse for any round hole or partial circle on the inclined plane. The minor axis of the 50° ellipse is aligned with the 90° perpendicular line. Always use the ellipse angle size that is nearest to the perpendicular line.

In Fig. 6-3, view 1, the visible end of the pipe is 45° from the horizontal, and this axis, which is perpendicular to the end of the pipe, crosses the protractor on the cylinder marked 55; so the 55° ellipse is used to show the end of the pipe.

In view 2 of Fig. 6-3, the angle bracket is 20° from the vertical, and the visible inclined plane is perpendicular to this surface. The 20° line crosses nearest the 50° ellipse; thus the 50° ellipse is used to show the hole on the bracket.

The holes on the object in view 3, Fig. 6-3, can be found with one setting of the protractor since one side is perpendicular to the other.

View 4, Fig. 6-3, shows a pipe in a horizontal position, and, as in view 1, there is no need to find

a 90° line since the end of the pipe is already perpendicular to the axis. The axis of the pipe crosses at the 20° ellipse; thus this is the proper ellipse to use to show the nonisometric end of the pipe.

In addition to an orthographic view of a bracket with inclined planes, Fig. 6-4 shows the step-by-step solution of the problem through use of the protractor to measure the angles and find the proper angle-size ellipses for the nonisometric planes.

The complete step-by-step solution for drawing a 45° pipe fitting, using the protractor to determine the angle and angle-size ellipse, is shown in Fig. 6-5. Axis *EC*, which is 45° from the vertical, passes directly over the small cylinder marked 55; therefore, the 55° ellipse is used to draw the end of the angle pipe.

Measuring a Compound Angle. The step-by-step solution for a bracket with a compound angle is shown in Fig. 6-6. The ellipse protractor is used to find the angles and the angle-size ellipse on the

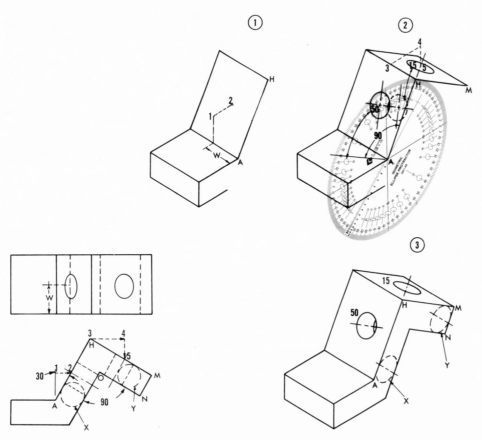

Fig. 6-4 Isometric ellipse protractor solutions.

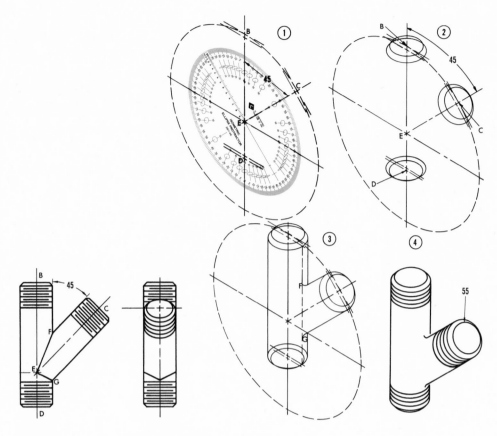

Fig. 6-5   Isometric ellipse protractor solutions.

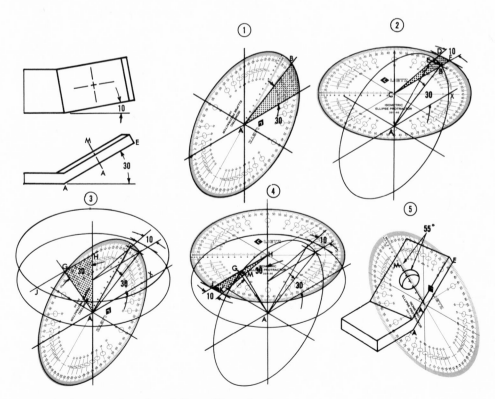

Fig. 6-6   Compound-angle solution with protractor.

oblique isometric plane. In this problem the third part of the protractor, the straight scale, is used. The following is the procedure for solving this problem with the protractor.

Step 1. Measure the 30° angle.

Step 2. Draw line *BC* parallel to *AX*. This locates the center *C* for the ellipse protractor in the horizontal position. Measure the 10° angle in the horizontal plane. Draw chord *DF* where the 10° angle lines cross the ellipse. Draw *BE* parallel to the chord *DF* through point *B*. From point *E*, where *EB* intersects line *CD*, draw line *AE*. This is the compound angle line for the edge *AE* of the bracket.

Step 3. Measure angle *GAH*. Line *GA* is 90° to line *AB*. Draw line *GH* from point *G* so that it is parallel to *AX*. Locate point *H*, which is the center for the horizontal position of the third ellipse.

Step 4. Measure the horizontal angle *JHK*. Notice that this 10° is in the opposite direction from the other 10°. Draw chord *JK* where the 10° angle lines cross the ellipse. Draw *GM* parallel to chord *JK* through point *G*. From point *M*, where line *GM* intersects line *HK*, draw line *MA*. This line is perpendicular to *AE* and is the axis for the hole on the bracket.

Step 5. Place the straight scale along line *MA* so that the center of the protractor is at *A*. Read the number, which is about 55, at point *M*. Use the 55° ellipse to draw the hole on the inclined plane.

Measuring a Compound-angle Pipe. The solution for the problem of how to find a compound angle on a pipe is shown in Fig. 6-7. The position of the pipe and the proper angle-size ellipse for the end of the pipe is decided by using the protractor. An angle of 30° was used for the vertical angle and

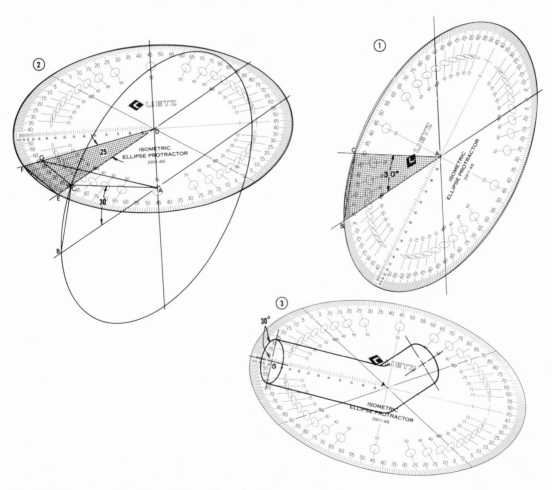

Fig. 6-7 Compound-angle solution with protractor.

an angle of 25° for the horizontal angle. The following is the solution for this problem.

Step 1. Measure the 30° angle *BAC*.

Step 2. Draw line *CD* parallel to *AB* and locate point *D*, which is the center for the protractor in measuring the horizontal 25° angle. Center the protractor at *D* and measure angle *FDE* 25°. Draw chord line *FE*. Draw *GC* parallel to *FE* from point *C*. From point *G* draw line *GA*. This is the axis for the compound-angle pipe.

Step 3. Place the straight scale of the protractor along line *GA* with the center at *A*. Read the number on the scale at point *G*; it is approximately 30°. This is the proper angle-size ellipse to use for the end of the pipe that is visible. Because *GA* is perpendicular to the end of the pipe, there is no need for the extra steps as shown in Fig. 6-6.

Questions

1. Explain the three parts of the Lietz isometric ellipse protractor.
2. How do you align the protractor?
3. What is the required first step when using the protractor to find the proper angle-size ellipse for a nonisometric plane?
4. Explain the procedure for finding a compound angle with the protractor.
5. What part of the protractor is used to find the angle-size ellipse for a compound surface?

Exercises

ISOMETRIC ELLIPSE PROTRACTOR
PROBLEMS

Refer to Group 5 Problems in Chap. 7. Use the isometric ellipse protractor to measure angles and the angle-size ellipse for inclined planes. Draw these problems in isometric using the isometric ellipse template and the proper angle-size ellipse for the inclined planes as determined by the isometric protractor.

When using the angle-size ellipses for the inclined planes, be sure to use the diameter size $1\frac{1}{4}$ times the diameter indicated on the blueprint, as explained in Chap. 4.

Draw the problems in the best possible position for showing the main characteristics of the object.

7 THE ELLIPSE AS A MEASURING DEVICE

The ellipse template is used in many ways in technical illustration. It is used not only for drawing circles, circular objects, holes, and round shafts, it serves an important, practical purpose as a measuring device.

Since the ellipse represents a circle in technical illustration, any radius or diameter of an ellipse represents equal distance. Therefore, given distances in any direction, regardless of whether the distance is along the axis of the drawing or parallel to the axis, can be measured with the ellipse. Distances on inclined planes involving one angle, and oblique planes involving angles in both horizontal and vertical planes, can be easily determined. Any diameter of the ellipse represents the same diameter of a circle. Any radius of an ellipse represents the equivalent radius of a circle. The radius or diameter of an ellipse can be used to measure the length of a line or the width of a plane; however, the right ellipse must be used and aligned properly with the minor axis, perpendicular to the plane.

Using the ellipse in the above manner eliminates the old conventional way of offset measuring or plotting for off-axes or inclined-plane measurements. This method of using the ellipse reduces the amount of time involved and is more accurate, especially when a number of measurements are desired along the same inclined plane or axes.

Measuring Lines and Surfaces. A rectangular solid appears in Fig. 7-1 with an isometric ellipse on each plane. All the radius lines of the ellipse represent equal distances on the plane of the ellipse. Lines *CA* and *DA* are nonisometric lines which cannot be measured with a scale. They would normally have to be plotted, but with the ellipse they can be easily measured.

The isometric box in Fig. 7-2 shows different diameter-size isometric ellipses on the surfaces. All the diameters represent equal distance. By using different diameter-size ellipses, any distance may be measured in any direction.

The box with the lid open (Fig. 7-3) shows use of the ellipse radius for measuring nonisometric lines *AC* and *AE*. The top orthographic view of the box is shown with the circle passing through the end of the box and the open lid. The isometric view is shown using the isometric ellipse for measuring the lid at various positions. The correct size isometric ellipse to use is equal to the circle diameter in the orthographic view.

The width of a plane surface using the ellipse is shown in Figs. 7-4 and 7-5. The spokes of a wheel can easily be measured with the ellipse indicated. Likewise the width of lugs is shown through use of the ellipse (Fig. 7-5). If the three lugs are the same width, only one ellipse may be placed at the center of the object with tangent lines drawn to the ellipse parallel to the axis of the lugs. The width of the lugs at *A* and *B* is nonisometric and cannot be measured with a scale. The use of the ellipse makes this a simple task.

The nonisometric length of lines on the bracket

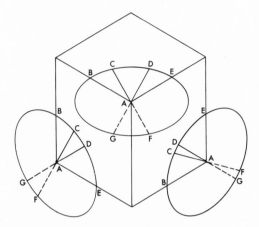

Fig. 7-1 Ellipse measuring.

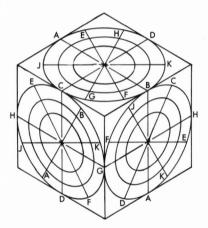

Fig. 7-2 Ellipse measuring.

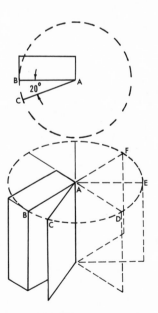

Fig. 7-3 Ellipse measuring.

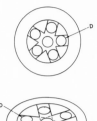

Fig. 7-4 Measuring with ellipse.

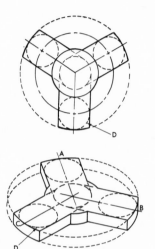

Fig. 7-5 Measuring with ellipse.

(Fig. 7-6) is easily determined by use of the ellipse. *AB* and *BC* are nonisometric lines and cannot be measured with a scale. The orthographic view is shown with the dashed-line circles, and the isometric solution is given. The ellipses are equal in diameter to the circles and therefore represent the proper length of the nonisometric lines. Distance *DE*, the diameter of the ellipse, is equal to *AB*, and *FE*, another diameter of the ellipse, is equal to *BC*. Of course, distance *AD*, a radius of the ellipse parallel to the inclined line, could be doubled to find the proper length of the nonisometric line *AB*. In like manner, *BF*, a radius of the ellipse, could be doubled to find the length of the nonisometric line *BC*. Various combinations of the ellipse can be used. The small dashed ellipses on the isometric view are the same diameter as the dashed circles on the orthographic view, and therefore this gives the proper thickness of the bracket.

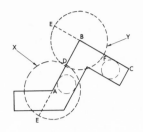

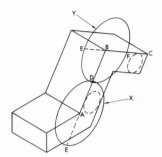

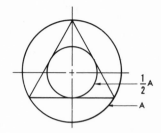

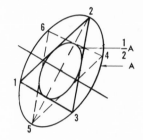

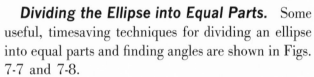

Fig. 7-6 Measuring with ellipse—inclined lines.

Fig. 7-7 Dividing ellipse.

Dividing the Ellipse into Equal Parts. Some useful, timesaving techniques for dividing an ellipse into equal parts and finding angles are shown in Figs. 7-7 and 7-8.

Figure 7-7 shows the frequently used, geometric-construction technique of inscribing a triangle in a circle to divide the circle into equal parts. For technical illustration simply substitute the ellipse for the circle and proceed accordingly. The ellipses here are isometric and therefore for an isometric illustration; however, by using the proper angle-size ellipses, you can apply the same technique to dimetric, trimetric, perspective, or nonisometric surfaces.

For better accuracy use a 2″ ellipse for *A*. The inner ellipse would of course be 1″. Draw tangent lines 1, 2, and 3 to locate the three equally-spaced points on the ellipse. To locate six equally-spaced points inscribe two triangles, etc.

View *A*, Fig. 7-8, shows four equally spaced points using the major and minor axes of the ellipse. These cannot be used if the four points are located off the axes. View *B* uses the major and minor axes of the ellipse and the 30° axis since this is isometric.

The hexagon template is used in views *C* and *D* and must be placed in the one proper position. It cannot be rotated in any position to determine

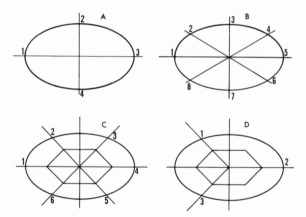

Fig. 7-8 Dividing ellipse.

these points. Of course the isometric protractor can be used but only for isometric illustrations.

A step-by-step illustration is shown in Fig. 7-9 of the use of the ellipse for measuring. In addition to measuring the length of lines and width of surfaces, the ellipse can be used to determine the angles for the three equally-spaced lugs. Ellipse *W* is half the diameter of ellipse *X*. Tangent lines are drawn to ellipse *W* to locate points *C*, *D*, and *E*. This is a simple method for dividing an ellipse into three equal parts, and it is an example of the use of the ellipse

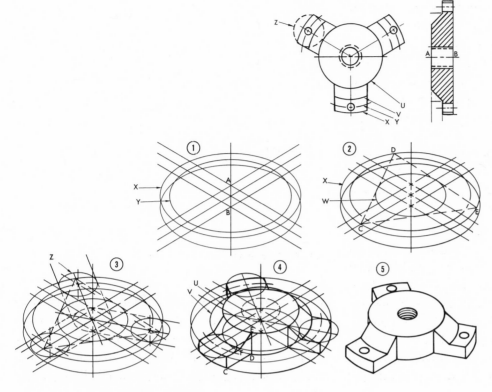

Fig. 7-9 Ellipse-measuring solution.

as a protractor for measuring angles. A more complete presentation and explanation of methods for using the ellipse as a protractor appear in a later section of this chapter.

Measuring Lines and Surfaces. The ellipse as a measuring device for lines and surfaces is especially effective, accurate, and timesaving in exploded views off axis, when single or multiple parts are shown along a nonisometric axis. Application of this technique is illustrated in Fig. 7-10, which shows orthographic views of a simple exploded assembly, the top and front view of the base, the orthographic parts exploded from the base, the assembly, and the isometric solution. The rectangular box with the ellipses shows the method used for measuring along this nonisometric line *UV*.

The isometric ellipses are placed with the minor axis perpendicular to the vertical plane of the exploded parts. The axis *UV* is determined and placed as shown on the ellipses. The diameter of the larger ellipse represents the length *A* of the orthographic view. The nonisometric distance *A* is obtained from the diameter of the ellipse along axis *UV* and is

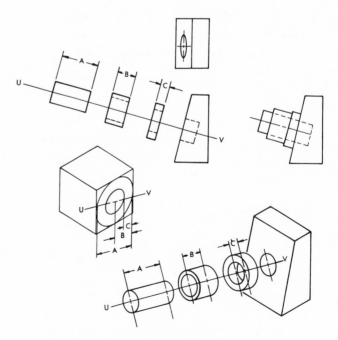

Fig. 7-10 Ellipse-measuring solution.

transferred by means of dividers to any position desired along non-isometric line *UV* of the exploded illustration. The non-isometric *B* distance is the radius along axis *UV* of the large ellipse. This distance represents orthographic distance *B*. The *C* distance is the difference between the large and small ellipse radius along *UV* and represents the orthographic distance *C*.

Another explanation of this technique is shown in Fig. 7-11. It is unnecessary to show an ellipse for every measurement, but one is used here to further explain the technique. In all these examples a partial scale could be established using various diameter-size ellipses to subdivide the scale. Figure 7-12 shows exploded parts and the measurements for a horizontal plane. The isometric ellipses are placed in a horizontal position on the horizontal surface of the rectangular box. The axis *YZ* in a horizontal plane is determined and placed as shown on the ellipses. The nonisometric distances *D*, *E*, and *F* are obtained from the proper combination of ellipses and are transferred by means of dividers to any position desired along nonisometric axis *YZ* of the exploded illustration. A number of measurements can be obtained from this combination of the two ellipses: the diameter of the ellipses, the radius of the ellipses, and any combination of their diameters or radii. As mentioned previously, a scale could easily be developed with ellipses to provide any measurement along the axis. The old plotting method for off-angle measurements

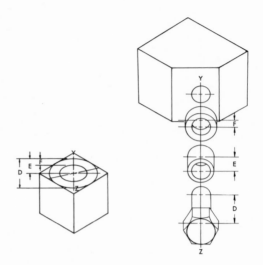

Fig. 7-12   Ellipse-measuring solution.

would take considerably more time and would probably not be as accurate. Another example of off-angle measurements, using the above techniques, is shown in Fig. 7-13. Measurements on oblique surfaces could be obtained in a similar manner if the angle-size ellipse were known for the oblique surface.

Another illustration showing an example of measuring with the ellipse appears in Fig. 7-14. The proper angle-size ellipse for the inclined planes is used. In this case the 50 and 15° ellipses are the proper angle-size ellipses for the two nonisometric planes. The proper angle-size ellipse is determined by one of several techniques explained later. If the proper angle-size ellipse for a surface is known, that ellipse may be used to measure on the surface by placing the ellipse in a position with the minor axis perpendicular to the surface. Notice that in order to obtain the 1″ nonisometric distance, a $1\frac{1}{4}$ angle ellipse must be used. It is necessary because this is an isometric illustration with a nonisometric plane. In this case the ellipse is placed flat on the required surface, whereas in the other previous examples it was placed perpendicular to the surface.

An example for measuring lines and angles of a tripod using the ellipse is shown in Fig. 7-15. Number 1 shows the top and front orthographic views. In view 2 the large dashed ellipse is equal in diameter to the dashed circle in the top orthographic view. This ellipse is divided into three equal parts, using one of the methods shown in Fig. 7-7

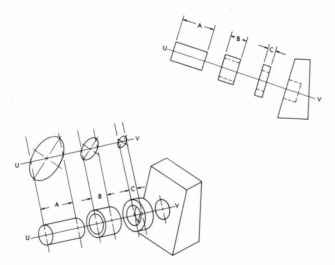

Fig. 7-11   Ellipse-measuring solution.

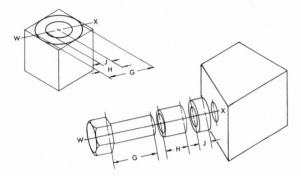

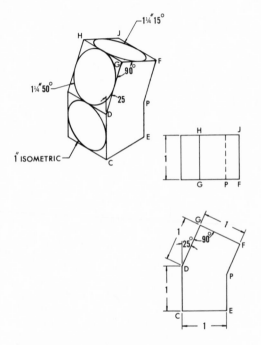

Fig. 7-13 Ellipse-measuring solution.

Fig. 7-14 Measuring with angle ellipse.

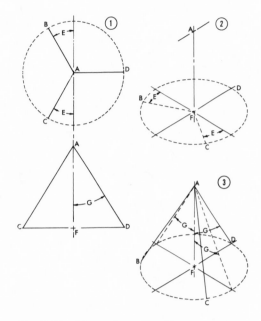

Fig. 7-15 Measuring with ellipse.

or view D, Fig. 7-8, and points B, C, and D are located. The height A-F is measured, and the lines AB, AC, and AD are drawn.

MEASURING THE LENGTH OF A COMPOUND-ANGLE LINE

Measuring the length of a nonisometric compound-angle line with the ellipse is shown in Fig. 7-16. The top and front orthographic views are shown with the step-by-step isometric solution. In step 1 the large ellipse X is equal in diameter to circle X; it is placed in a vertical plane to locate point C. The 30° angle can be obtained using the

ellipse protractor (see Chap. 6). In step 2 draw the isometric line EC from point C, locating point E on the vertical axis. Point E locates the center for the ellipse in the horizontal plane. The diameter of this ellipse centered at E is equal to an ellipse that will pass through point C. In other words, point C rotates in a circular path represented by the ellipse. The 15° angle is determined in the horizontal plane using the protractor locating point D. A line is drawn from point D to A. This is the compound-angle line for the illustration and the proper length.

USING THE ELLIPSE AS A PROTRACTOR

One can use the ellipse as a protractor by measuring angles on an orthographic circle and projecting the angles to the ellipse, as shown in Fig. 7-17. This circle-projection method can also be used for dimetric, trimetric, and perspective if the appropriate angle-size ellipse is used instead of isometric. The illustrations here are isometric.

In order to maintain accuracy, use a $1\frac{1}{2}''$ ellipse or, better still, a 2" ellipse. Remember that the major-axis distance of the ellipse must be the same as the diameter of the circle. In other words, if this system is used for isometric drawings and if a $1\frac{1}{2}''$ isometric ellipse is used, the circle will be $1\frac{7}{8}$ ($1\frac{1}{2}$ × $1\frac{1}{4}$). For dimetric, trimetric, and perspective

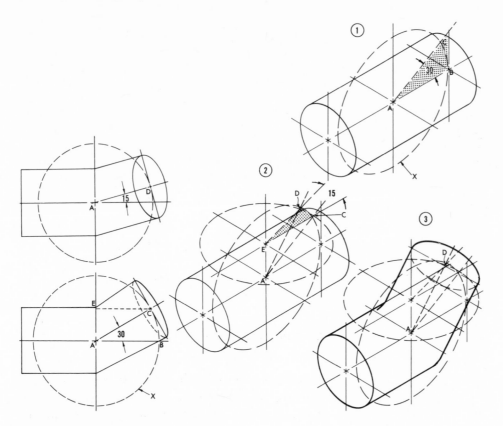

Fig. 7-16   Measuring compound distance.

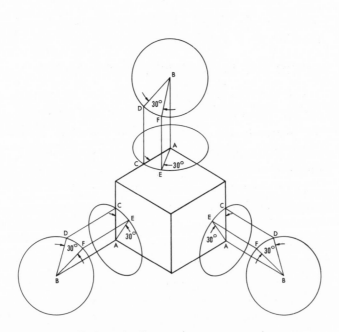

Fig. 7-17   Circle-projection angle measurement.

drawings use the proper angle-size ellipse for the plane where the angle is to be measured. (See Chap. 11.)

A front-view orthographic drawing is shown of a box with the lid open 30° (Fig. 7-18). The circle-projection solution is shown with the lid open at an angle of 30°. In the orthographic drawing a circle is drawn with the center at D and with the circumference passing through points E and F. The following is the procedure for solving this problem for an isometric drawing.

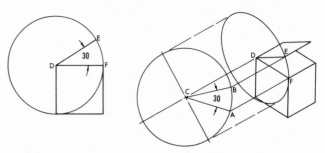

Fig. 7-18   Circle-projection angle measurement.

1. Place a 2″ isometric ellipse centered at *D* with the minor axis perpendicular to the vertical plane of the box, in other words, parallel to the 30° axis *CD*.

2. Draw the 30° line *CD*.

3. Draw the circle centered at *C*. Remember this circle is equal in diameter to the major-axis distance of the isometric ellipse used, since this is an isometric drawing.

4. From point *F* draw the 30° line *FA* to locate point *A* on the circle. This is the base line for measuring the 30° angle.

5. Measure the 30° angle *ACB*.

6. Project point *B* along a 30° line, locating point *E* on the ellipse. Angle *FDE* is a 30° isometric angle. This procedure solves not only for the 30° isometric angle, but for the proper length of the nonisometric line *DE*, since the ellipse used is the proper size for the circle shown on the orthographic drawing. In this illustration we have solved for the isometric angle, as well as for the proper length of the nonisometric line *DE*, by using the ellipse as a measuring device.

Finding Angle-size Ellipse on Inclined Plane.

The angle-size ellipse for the inclined plane of the object in Fig. 7-19 is solved by using the circle-projection method and triangle solution. Use the following procedure:

Step 1. Place a 2″ isometric ellipse, centered at *A*, with the minor axis perpendicular to the plane of the angle.

Draw the 30° line *AB*.

Draw the circle, centered at *B*, an indefinite distance from the ellipse.

From point *C* draw the line *CD* parallel to *AB*, locating point *D* on the circle. This is the base line for measuring the 55° angle.

Step 2. Measure the 55° angle *DBE*.

Project point *E* along a 30° line, locating point *F* on the ellipse. Angle *FAC* is an isometric 55° angle.

Step 3. Measure the 90° angle *EBG* on the circle. To find the angle-size ellipse on an inclined plane, you must find the line that is perpendicular

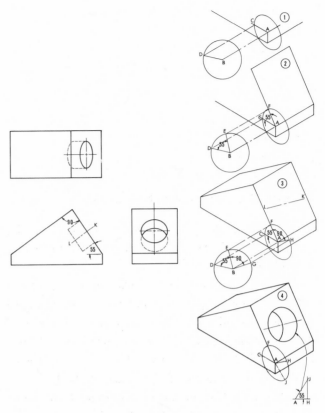

Fig. 7-19 Circle-projection problem solution.

to the inclined plane because the axis for the hole is 90° to the plane.

Project point *G* along a 30° line to point *H* on the ellipse.

Draw line *HA* which represents a perpendicular to *AF*.

Step 4. Place line *AH*, the radius of the ellipse that is perpendicular to the inclined plane, along the base of a right triangle.

Draw a perpendicular of indefinite length from point *H*.

Set a pair of dividers using distance *AJ*, half the major axis of the ellipse, and with one point of the divider at *A*, mark the distance *AJ* on the vertical line.

Measure angle *HAJ*. It is 55°, the proper angle-size for an ellipse to use for the hole on the inclined plane of the bracket. This is a mathematical solution of a right triangle using the true radius of the ellipse with a foreshortened radius.

Figures 7-20 and 7-21 show the construction of several examples using the circle-projection method

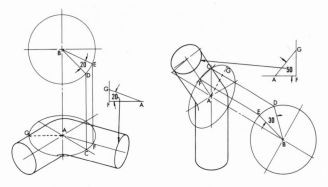

Fig. 7-20   Circle-projection problem solution.

for finding angles and angle-size ellipses for the inclined planes.   These are isometric drawings using the ellipse for measuring.

Figure 7-22 shows the construction of a problem using the circle-projection technique for finding angles and angle-size ellipses on inclined planes.   In addition, this illustration shows how to measure inclined lines using the ellipse as a measuring device.   The diameter of the ellipse centered at A is equal to the length of line HA and HM in the orthographic front view. The diameter FG (step 2) of the ellipse is parallel

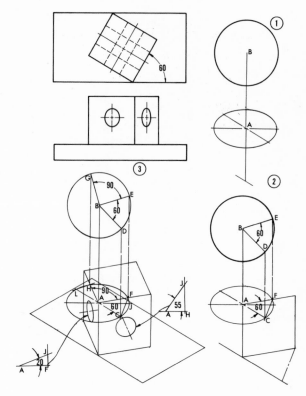

Fig. 7-21   Circle-projection problem solution.

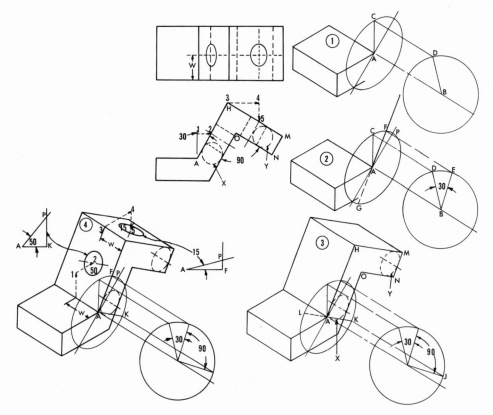

Fig. 7-22   Measuring angle-size ellipse.

to the line *HA* (step 3) and therefore is the proper length of line *HA*. The diameter *LK* of the ellipse (step 3) is parallel to line *HM* and therefore is the proper length of line *HM* (step 3). The thickness of the bracket *MN* is determined by placing ellipse *Y*, which is the same size as the orthographic circle *Y*, with the minor axis perpendicular to the plane, and drawing lines tangent to the ellipse. In like manner, ellipse *X* is used to determine the thickness of the bracket. The location of the center of the holes is plotted by using points 1, 2, 3, 4, and 5 in step 4. These points are obtained from the orthographic views and plotted on the isometric view.

The 15° and 50° angle-size ellipses in step 4 are solved by the two triangles as indicated.

Compound Angles. A compound angle can be solved if the ellipse is used as a protractor, as illustrated in Fig. 7-23. The 15° angle is solved in steps 1 and 2 as previously explained. To rotate the vertical part of this object, use a 45° ellipse since this was found to be the proper angle-size ellipse in step 2 for the hole in the inclined horizontal plane. The procedure for steps 3 and 4 is as follows:

Step 3. Center the 45° ellipse at *J* and draw line *JS* parallel to *FA* in step 2.

Draw a circle centered at *S* and equal in diameter to the 45° ellipse.

Draw line *TU* from point *T*.

Step 4. Measure the 15° angle, locating point *V*.

Draw line *VW* parallel to *SJ*, and draw line *JZ* through point *W*, which locates the 15° isometric rotation of this line.

Measure the 90° angle on the circle, locating point *X*.

Project point *X* to the ellipse locating point *Y*. Draw line *JY*. This is the axis for the 15° ellipse.

Solve for the angle-size ellipse, as explained previously, using triangle *YJ*2.

COMBINING TECHNIQUES

The example in Fig. 7-24 utilizes all the techniques that have been explained for measuring isometric angles and length of nonisometric lines and solving for the proper angle-size ellipse for the hole on the nonisometric plane. All these techniques can be easily combined to solve this orthographic problem.

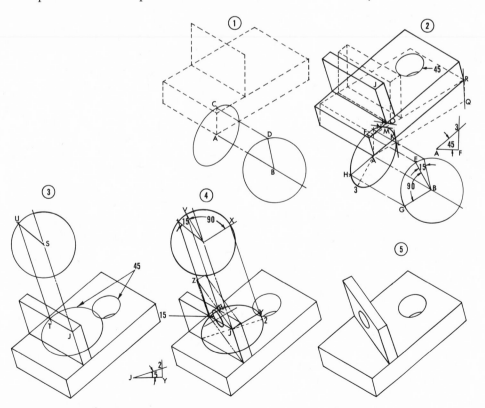

Fig. 7-23 Measuring angle-size ellipse.

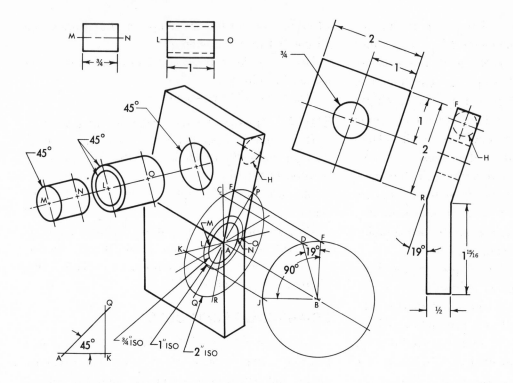

Fig. 7-24 Circle-projection problem solution.

SIMPLIFIED CIRCLE PROJECTION

Figure 7-25 shows, in the circle-projection technique, how the circle can be combined with the ellipse. Compare this illustration with Fig. 7-24.

ELLIPSE ON SPHERE FOR MEASURING

A combination of the ellipse and sphere may be used, as in Fig. 7-26, to solve angles, angle-size ellipse on inclined planes, and length of lines. This is an isometric illustration; however, as in the other techniques, a dimetric, trimetric, or perspective illustration can be solved using a similar procedure. Instead of using the isometric ellipse, use the proper angle-size ellipses for the different planes.

In view 1, Fig. 7-26, the 20° angle is measured and the 20° angle-size ellipse is obtained in the following manner.

1. Draw two isometric ellipses centered at A and perpendicular to each other. Use a large diameter, at least 2″, for accuracy.
2. Draw the sphere with the circle tangent to the major-axis points of the ellipses.
3. Draw the 30° isometric axis AC, and draw a 30° line from point C intersecting the circle at D. Draw line DA. This is the base line from

which to measure the 20° angle on the circle.

4. Measure the 20° angle DAE on the circle.
5. From point E, draw a 30° line locating point B on the ellipse. Draw line BA to form the isometric angle CAB. Draw AK half the major axis of the ellipse.
6. Draw the triangle BAK using the foreshortened radius and the true radius of the sphere to obtain the 20°.

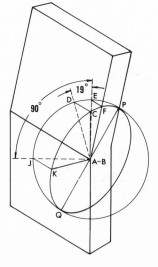

Fig. 7-25 Simplified circle projection.

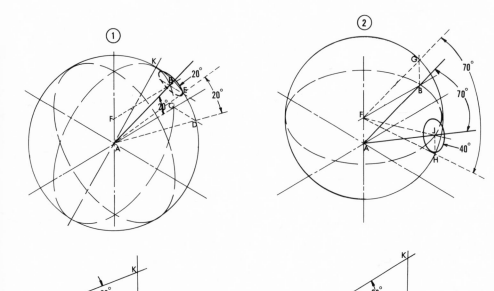

Fig. 7-26 Sphere measurement.

View 2 of Fig. 7-26 shows how the line *AB* in view 1 can be rotated 70° in the horizontal plane to obtain the compound angle *JAB*, the proper length of the compound angle axis *AJ*, and the proper angle-size ellipse 40°, perpendicular to axis *AJ*. Proceed as follows:

1. Line *BF* is obtained in view 1 by drawing a 30° line from point *B* to the vertical, locating *F*. This is the center for the large isometric ellipse in the horizontal plane and for the circle used to measure the 70° angle.
2. Draw the isometric ellipse centered at *F* that will pass through point *B*.
3. Project point *B* on a vertical line to the circle, locating point *G*, and draw *GF*. *GF* is the base line for measuring the 70° on the circle.
4. Measure the 70° angle *GFH* on the circle.
5. Project point *H* on a vertical line to the ellipse, locating *J*.
6. Draw line *JA* to form the compound angle *JAB*.
7. Draw the triangle *JAK* to obtain the 40° angle-size ellipse. Layout *AJ*, the radius of the sphere which is perpendicular to the ellipse, on the base of the triangle. Draw a perpendicular from *J*. Set the divider with distance *AK* (view 1), and with *A* as center, locate *K* on the vertical. Measure the 38° angle and use the

40° ellipse (nearest 5°) to draw the ellipse centered at *J*. Be sure the minor axis of the ellipse is aligned with axis *AJ*.

BOX METHOD FOR SOLVING ANGLE ELLIPSE

An eyeball method for finding the proper angle-size ellipse for an inclined plane is illustrated in Fig. 7-27. This is for a nonisometric plane; however, this same technique can be used in other types of illustrations. The eyeball technique is used in some illustration groups and requires the technical illustrator to fit the proper ellipse in a nonisometric square. The procedure follows:

Step 1. Draw a 1″ isometric ellipse, centered at *A*, which is the size of the hole on the orthographic view.

Draw an isometric square around the ellipse.

Layout the angles *BAC* and *DAE* by measurements from the front view.

Step 2. Draw a 1″ isometric ellipse centered at *F*, and draw the rotated isometric square, making *FH* parallel to *AC*. Complete the isometric square and transfer axis *AE* from step 1 to step 2.

Step 3. By trial and error, find a 1¼″ angle-size ellipse that will fit in the square when the minor axis

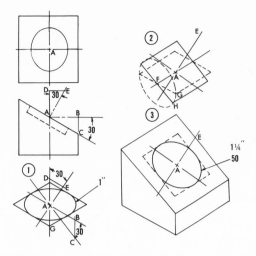

Fig. 7-27 Solving angle-size ellipse—box method.

is aligned with *AE*, the line perpendicular to the surface.

The $1\frac{1}{4}$ ellipse must be used because this is a nonisometric surface, and an angle-size ellipse does not account for the oversize as the isometric ellipse does. The perpendicular *AE* must be found because

the minor axis of the ellipse must be aligned with the perpendicular line.

Questions

1. Explain how the ellipse can be used for measuring nonisometric lines.
2. Describe three ways to divide an ellipse into equal parts.
3. Name the technique for measuring angles with the ellipse.
4. Describe the concentric-ellipse method for dividing an ellipse into equal parts.
5. Make a nonisometric scale for parts located on the same nonisometric axis.
6. Explain how the proper angle-size ellipse can be used to measure on a nonisometric plane.
7. Why is the diameter of an angle-size ellipse multiplied by $1\frac{1}{4}$ when used on a nonisometric plane?
8. Explain the triangle solution for finding the proper angle-size ellipse on an inclined plane.
9. Describe the eyeball method for finding the proper angle-size ellipse on an inclined plane.

PROBLEMS: GROUP 5
Brackets—Ellipse as a Measuring Device

Draw these problems in isometric, using the circle-projection method for measuring angles and the angle-size ellipses on the inclined planes. Use the isometric ellipse to measure the nonisometric lines as explained in the chapter. When using the angle ellipse on nonisometric planes, remember to use the diameter size that is $1\frac{1}{4}$ times the indicated diameter on the blueprint.

Compare these illustrations with the same illustrations as they are made using the isometric ellipse protractor.

The Hexangle template is used to draw the hexagon bolts and nuts. The proper Hexangle size required is equal to $1\frac{1}{4}$ times the indicated diameter of the bolt. See Chaps. 4 and 8 for an explanation of this fact. Remember, these hexagons are on a nonisometric plane, and the isometric hexagon template cannot be used. Draw one of the problems with the hexagon bolt and nut, using the simplified method for drawing the hexagon. The diameter size of the ellipse to use for the hex is twice the diameter of the bolt. Review the explanation for this procedure.

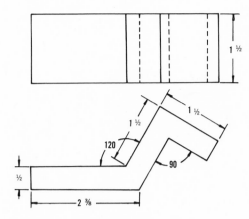

Prob. 5-1 Angle bracket.

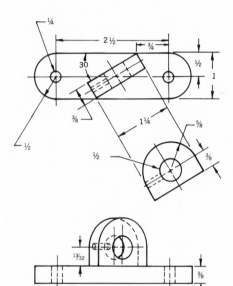

Prob. 5-2 Lug angle.

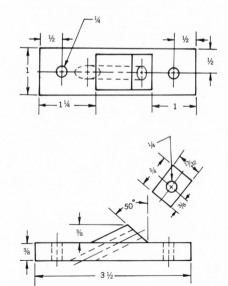

Prob. 5-3 Angle base.

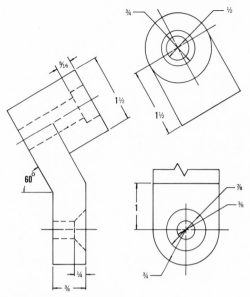

Prob. 5-4 Post angle.

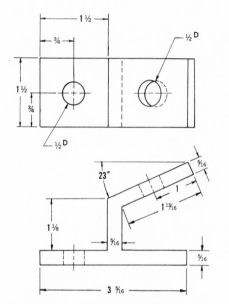

Prob. 5-5 Base angle plate.

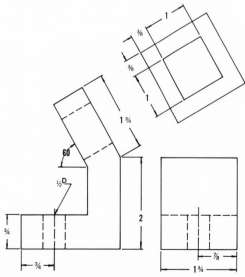

Prob. 5-6 Angle holder.

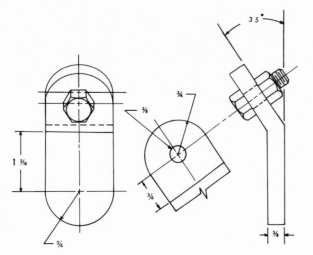

Prob. 5-7 Angle subassembly.

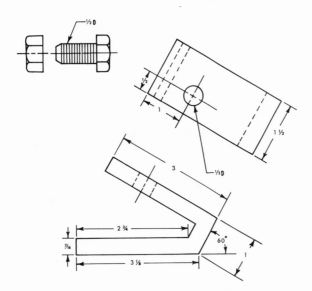

Prob. 5-8 Base angle assembly.

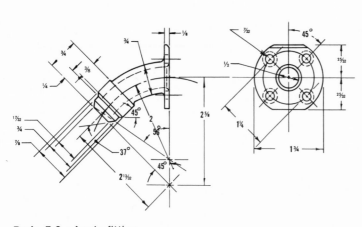

Prob. 5-9 Angle fitting.

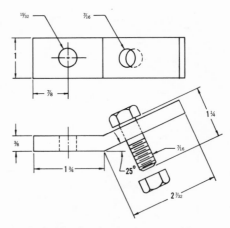

Prob. 5-10 Angle clamp assembly.

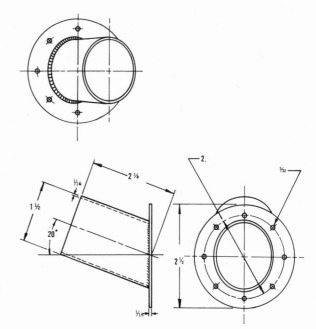

Prob. 5-11 Housing angle.

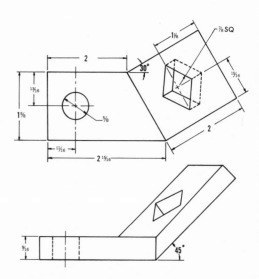

Prob. 5-12 Bracket brace.

8

FASTENERS AND SPRINGS

There are many different types of fasteners; however, the most frequently used basic types are discussed here. Techniques used for drawing the hexagon head, square head, round head, fillister head, flat head, carriage head, and Phillips head are illustrated. The ellipse template is used to show the techniques for drawing these fasteners.

HEXAGON HEAD

The hexagon head may be made by using the isometric hexagon template or the Hexangle template. The proper use of these templates is discussed in Chap. 3. This discussion and the illustrations are concerned with the construction of simplified hexagons using the ellipse templates. In many cases the simplified hexagon is constructed, especially if the hexagon is small in size. Most places make a simplified hexagon, using the ellipse, when the diameter of the bolt is $\frac{3}{4}''$ or less.

The illustrations in Fig. 8-1 show an isometric view of the hexagon bolt and nut in the horizontal and the vertical planes. By rotating the book, one can obtain a representation of the hexagon on the other axes. An orthographic view of the most common hexagon bolt and nut is shown. The thickness of the bolt head is approximately $\frac{2}{3}$ the diameter of the bolt. The

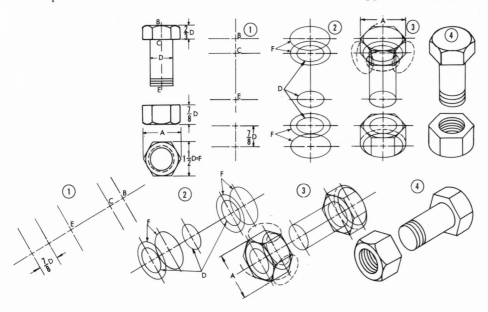

Fig. 8-1 Hex-head bolt and nut.

thickness of the hexagon nut is approximately $\frac{7}{8}$ the diameter of the bolt.

The diameter size F of the large ellipses in step 2 is equal to the distance across the flats of the hexagon or about $1\frac{1}{2}$ times the diameter of the bolt. In step 3 the corners of the hexagon are located, and the chamfer is drawn, using the ellipses as shown. In many cases neither the chamfer nor the flat sides are shown, especially if the bolt is small, $\frac{5}{16}$ or less. (See Fig. 8-2.) The inner corners of the hex are located slightly within the exterior lines of the body of the bolt. When the bolt is small, these corners are practically in line with the exterior lines of the body of the bolt. From the inner corners of the hexagon in step 3 draw lines tangent to the ellipse, locating the exterior corners of the hexagon, distance A. Note that the actual distance A in step 3 is greater than the distance A in the orthographic view, because this is an isometric drawing. A small arc of an ellipse is used to connect the exterior corners with the large ellipse, and two of the corners disappear from view, as shown in step 4.

SIMPLIFIED HEXAGON

Frequently hexagons are made in a simplified manner using the ellipse templates (Fig. 8-2). An isometric illustration is shown of a hexagon nut and

bolt head in Fig. 8-2 without any chamfer or flat sides.

The diameter sizes of the ellipses at C and D are $1\frac{5}{8}$ times the diameter of the bolt. This measurement is equal to the distance across the corners of the hexagon. Distance AB is $\frac{7}{8}$ times the diameter of the bolt since this is approximately equal to the thickness of a hexagon nut. Distance EF is $\frac{2}{3}$ times the diameter of the bolt, and this is approximately equal to the thickness of a hexagon-head bolt. Notice that the corners of the hexagon are located slightly inside the diameter of the hole or body of the bolt.

To make a simplified hexagon for a dimetric, trimetric, or perspective illustration, use the same procedure but substitute the proper angle-size ellipse for the isometric ellipse.

Simplified Hexagon—Nonisometric Surface. To draw a simplified hexagon on a nonisometric surface, you must use the proper angle-size ellipse. (See Fig. 8-3.) Use an angle ellipse with a diameter twice the size of the bolt to obtain the major diameter across the corners. For example, to make a hexagon for a $\frac{1}{2}''$ bolt or nut, use an ellipse $1\frac{1}{4}$ times the diameter, or $\frac{5}{8}$, because you are using an angle ellipse on a nonisometric surface. This amount must then be multiplied by $1\frac{5}{8}$, since this is the distance across the corners of a hexagon, and the ellipse must be equal

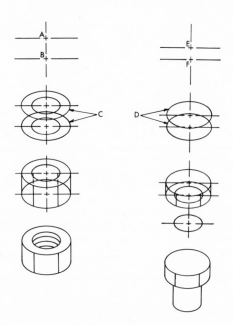

Fig. 8-2   Simplified hex using ellipse.

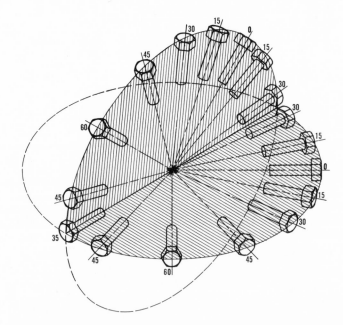

Fig. 8-3   Hexagon angle size.

to the distance across the corners. Therefore, $\frac{5}{8}$ times $1\frac{5}{8}$ is $\frac{65}{64}$ or about 2 times $\frac{1}{2}$.

SQUARE HEAD

The method used for drawing a square-head bolt and nut is shown in Fig. 8-4. The distance across the corners of the square head is equal to twice the diameter of the bolt, and the distance across the flats is equal to $1\frac{1}{2}$ times the diameter. The thickness of the head is about $\frac{2}{3}$ times the diameter of the bolt, and the thickness of the nut is about $\frac{7}{8}$ times the diameter. Of course there are special square head bolts and nuts that may not have these same dimensions. When chamfer is shown, as in step 3, a partial ellipse is used as an arc to connect the exterior corners tangent to ellipse B. When the bolt is small, less than $\frac{5}{16}''$, chamfer is normally omitted. In some cases it is omitted for all sizes, especially when considerable reduction is made on the final illustration. The chamfer on the horizontal nut in step 4 is drawn using a 45° ellipse. Be sure to have the thickness the same at the three visible corners. The four corners of the square head are located at the major- and minor-axis points of the ellipse.

FILLISTER HEAD

The conventional fillister head (see Fig. 8-5) has the diameter of the head equal to $1\frac{1}{2}$ times the diameter of the bolt. The thickness of the head is about $\frac{2}{3}$ times the diameter of the bolt. The notch of the head is drawn with an ellipse about four times the diameter of the bolt. Always place the notch along one of the axes of the illustration to avoid distortion. (See Fig. 8-6.) The depth of the notch in fillister bolts $\frac{5}{16}$ or less is usually made as a single line, because when reduced, the "fill-in" would make two lines appear as one anyway (see Fig. 8-9).

If no reduction in size is anticipated, the notch may be shown as two arcs. The large circle in step 2 may be omitted. It is shown here only to indicate that the top of the fillister is a small part of a sphere.

ROUND HEAD

The head diameter of the conventional round-head bolt is about $1\frac{1}{2}$ times the diameter of the bolt. The head is about one-half a sphere as shown in steps 2 and 3, Fig. 8-7. There are many types which would vary in size, and they would have to be drawn accord-

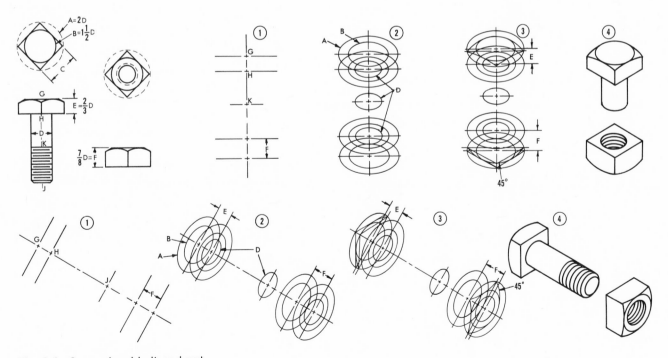

Fig. 8-4 Square-head bolt and nut.

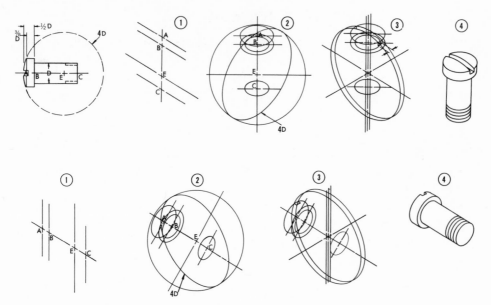

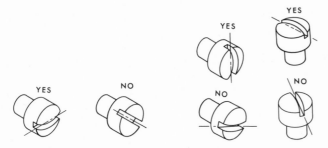

Fig. 8-5 Fillister-head bolt.

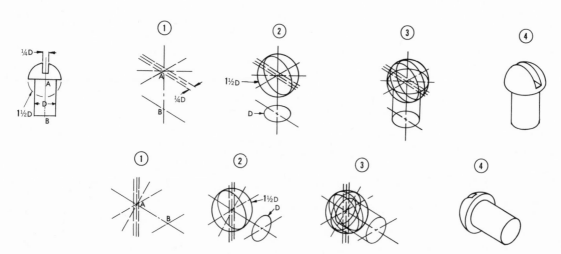

Fig. 8-6 Notch position.

Fig. 8-7 Round-head fastener.

ingly; however, this is the basic type, and, generally speaking, this is the technique used for the majority of round heads.

The notch is drawn using an ellipse that is the same diameter as the head, since the notch is on the exterior of the sphere. The width of the notch is about $\frac{1}{4}$ the diameter, and the depth of the notch is about $\frac{1}{2}$ the diameter of the bolt. Again, as with the fillister, the notch may be drawn with a single line if the fastener is small. (See Fig. 8-9.) A round-head rivet is drawn about the same way except that the notch is eliminated. Notice that part of the head is made with half of a circle and the other with half of an ellipse. This is the technique used when eyeballing.

FLAT HEAD

The diameter of the conventional flat head (see Fig. 8-8) is approximately twice the diameter of the bolt. The thickness of the head is about $\frac{1}{2}$ the diameter of the bolt. The depth of the notch is $\frac{1}{4}$ the diameter of the bolt. Show the notch along one of the axes of the illustration (see Fig. 8-6), and, again, if the bolt is small, show the notch as a single line (see Fig. 8-9). The angle E on the head will vary with the different styles.

CARRIAGE HEAD

One common type of carriage bolt is shown in Fig. 8-10. There are several variations; however, we are mainly interested in the techniques used for drawing the head. The diameter of the head is about twice

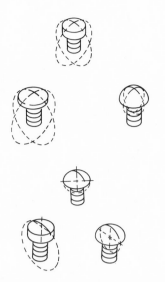

Fig. 8-9 Simplified fasteners.

the diameter of the bolt. The thickness of the head is about $\frac{1}{2}$ the diameter of the bolt. The top of the head is made with the proper size ellipse. The large circle X can be omitted since it is shown here only to demonstrate to the reader that the head is part of a sphere. A small arc Y is drawn with ellipse Z to suggest the curvature of the head. Place this arc along one of the axes of the illustration.

PHILLIPS HEAD

The Phillips head is constructed with techniques similar to the fillister-head and flat-head techniques, depending on whether it is round or flat. The notches, however, are in the shape of a cross. (See Fig. 8-9.)

THREADS

Threads are made with the ellipse template, as shown in Fig. 8-11. In most cases, no attempt is made to distinguish between extra-fine, fine, or regular-type threads. The spacing of the distance between threads is important, and this spacing must be equal distance. The amount of space between the threads is governed by the diameter size of the bolt and nut and by the amount of reduction in the size of the illustration, but it is never less than $\frac{1}{16}''$ because of fill-in when the size is reduced. Scratching short marks on the ellipse templates (Fig. 8-11 a and b) along the minor axis is one way of maintaining equal

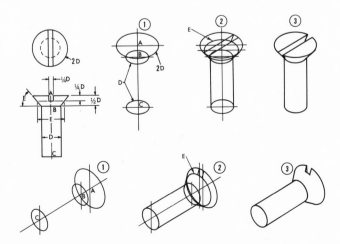

Fig. 8-8 Flat-head fastener.

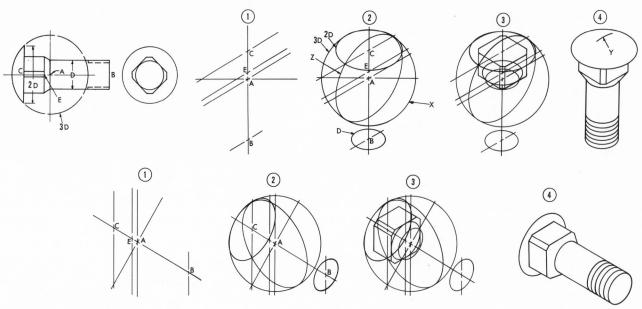

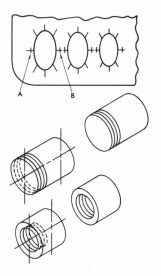

Fig. 8-10 Carriage-head bolt.

Fig. 8-11 Thread construction.

spacing. There is no need to show the exact number of threads per inch; however, if, for example, the bolt is threaded halfway, show the threads accordingly. Align the ellipse with the minor axis parallel with the axis of the bolt or nut. Do not show the threads at an angle and do not show the root of the thread. Use an ellipse equal to the diameter of the bolt. Some illustration groups request that the hole for a threaded fastener be made slightly larger than the fastener to avoid the optical illusion of its appearing too small.

In the majority of cases, however, this is not done. When fasteners are small, threads are sometimes omitted, since most illustrations are reduced in size. This would cause a problem of fill-in in which the threads would appear as a black spot if placed less than $\frac{1}{16}''$ apart.

WASHERS

The conventional washers are made with the inside diameter equal to the diameter of bolt and the outside diameter equal to 2 times the diameter of bolt. The typical flat washer is normally made with a heavy line to show thickness. (See Fig. 5-38.)

An illustration of a lock washer is shown in Fig. 8-12. Tilt one end of the ellipse at a slight angle to get the proper effect.

SPRING TEMPLATE

The step-by-step techniques for using a spring template are shown in Fig. 8-13. This spring template (Fig. 8-14) may be used for all types of illustrations. It is not designated as an isometric spring template or as for any other type of illustration. The diameter indicated on the template is the outside diameter of the spring. Part *A* is for the outside diameter, and part *B* for the inside. If a spring is to be shown by only a single line, which is the case many times, the *A* part or the *B* part may be used

Fig. 8-12   Drawing lock washer.

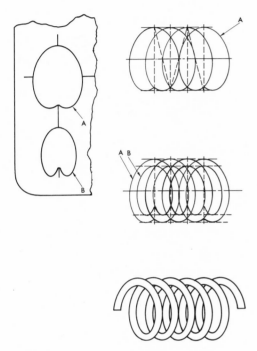

Fig. 8-13   How to use spring template.

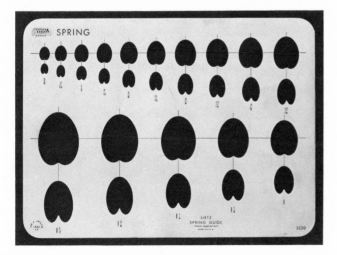

Fig. 8-14   Spring template. (Courtesy: The Lietz Co.)

separately depending upon the size desired. In this step-by-step illustration, a double-line spring is shown. To draw a left-hand spring, turn the template upside down.

If a different type of spring is desired, compressed or extended further, the ellipse template is used as shown in Fig. 8-15.

DRAWING SPRING WITH ELLIPSE

The ellipse template can be used to make a spring, as illustrated in Fig. 8-15. Use an angle-size ellipse for the outer part of the spring, depending upon the amount of extension. Select a diameter size that will remain within the outer diameter construction lines. The inner part of the spring can be drawn using an angle ellipse 5° less than the outer ellipse.

Questions

1. What diameter-size ellipse is used to draw a simplified hexagon?
2. What is the thickness of a hexagon-head bolt?
3. What is the thickness of a hexagon nut?
4. How do you determine the location of a hexagon corner when using the simplified method of construction?
5. When drawing a simplified hexagon on a non-isometric surface, what diameter-size ellipse is used? Explain.
6. What angle-size ellipse is used to draw the chamfer on a square nut?
7. When should the notch in a fillister head be drawn with only a single line?
8. Describe a simplified method for drawing a round-head bolt or rivet.
9. Explain a practical method for spacing the threads on a bolt.
10. How would you draw a left-hand spring using the spring template?

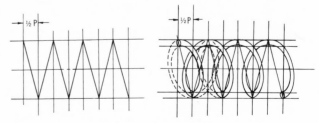

Fig. 8-15   Drawing spring with ellipse.

PROBLEMS: GROUP 6
Fasteners and Springs

Draw isometric views of these problems. Draw the hexagon bolts and nuts, first using the simplified method with the isometric ellipse template. Use the isometric hexagon template to draw these same problems. Review the information regarding the use of the isometric hexagon template in order to obtain the proper size. Draw the hexagon bolt and nut, using the ellipse, and show the chamfer. Follow the step-by-step method explained in the chapter.

Use the ellipse to draw the fillister, carriage head, round head, flat head, square head, and Phillips head.

Use the spring template to draw the spring. Draw one spring in a left-hand position by turning the spring template upside down.

Draw a spring using the ellipse template and follow the technique explained in the chapter.

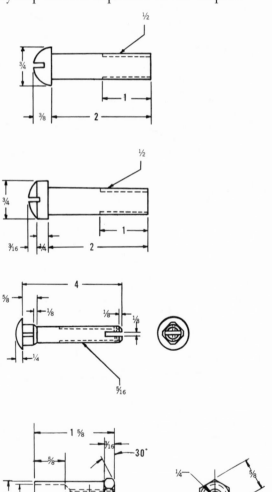

Prob. 6-1   Fasteners.

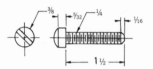

Prob. 6-2   Fillister-head bolt.

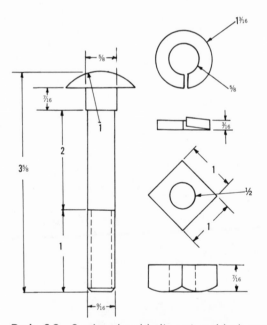

Prob. 6-3   Carriage-head bolt—nut and lock washer.

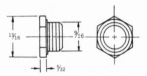

Prob. 6-4   Hex plug.

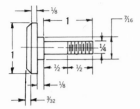

Prob. 6-5   Chamfer-head fastener.

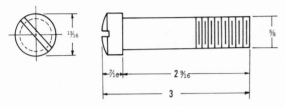

Prob. 6-6   Fillister-head bolt.

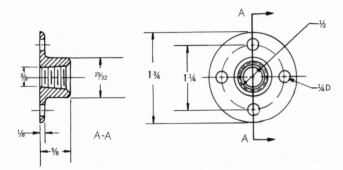

Prob. 6-7   Pipe plate.

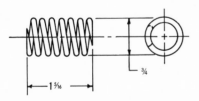

Prob. 6-8   Spring.

Prob. 6-9   Flat-head rivet.

Prob. 6-10   Round-head rivet.

Prob. 6-11   Truss-head rivet.

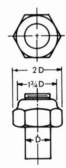

Prob. 6-13   B nut.

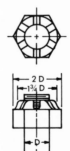

Prob. 6-12   Castle nut.

9 LAYOUT AND CONSTRUCTION METHODS

Layout may be defined as "an accurate plan of an illustration showing easily understood views, proper placement of parts, details, assemblies, spots, or sections, and the necessary index numbers, leaders, and callouts to identify the object clearly."

Layout is very important in making a satisfactory technical illustration. Many technical illustrators do not realize the importance of proper layout, and a poor layout will ruin an otherwise good illustration.

Good balance on the page is of primary importance. The object must be shown in a desirable position without the confusion caused by the reckless placement of parts. The technical illustrator must remember that he is basically a communicator, a translator who is preparing a picture for many people who may have limited technical knowledge.

In exploded illustrations, parts must be placed in a position that will ensure complete understanding of the shape and location of each part. Care must be taken that no part obscures another part. Parts may overlap if no detail is concealed. In fact, in some cases it may be desirable to overlap parts for a better understanding of the assembly of the parts. In some instances the technical illustrator may not be allowed to overlap parts. Frequently he is controlled by given specifications or by the available space on the page.

Technical illustrations may be classified by several general layout patterns: rectangular, center line,

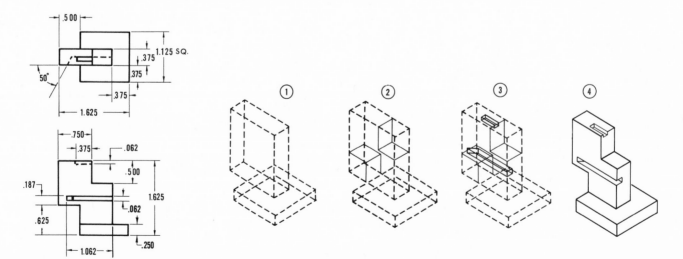

Fig. 9-1 Rectangular construction.

cyclindrical, conical, spherical, sectional, phantom, irregular, gear, pipe, and fasteners. Most illustrations are made up of a combination of these.

RECTANGULAR LAYOUT

Rectangular layouts usually require that the object be boxed in and that the box then be cut apart into several geometric shapes. These rectangular shapes may be classified as regular horizontal and vertical planes, inclined planes, or oblique planes.

Figure 9-1 illustrates the step-by-step method for the construction of a typical rectangular-shaped object with horizontal and vertical planes.

Inclined Plane. Figure 9-2 shows a step-by-step method for construction of an object with an inclined plane. Some plotting is necessary to locate the points of the inclined plane and the location of the center lines for the holes.

The object shown in Fig. 9-3 is mainly a rectangular layout but also requires some center-line location and use of the ellipse templates. Whenever ellipses are used, be sure to draw two center lines, the major axis and the minor axis, for accurate construction.

Oblique Plane. An oblique plane layout is shown in Fig. 9-4.

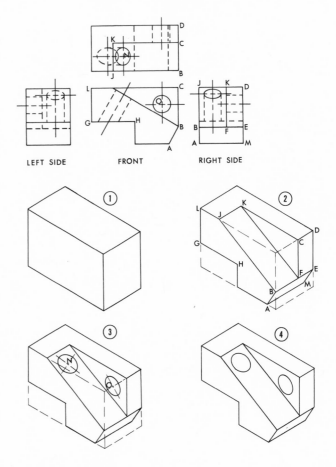

Fig. 9-2 Inclined-plane construction.

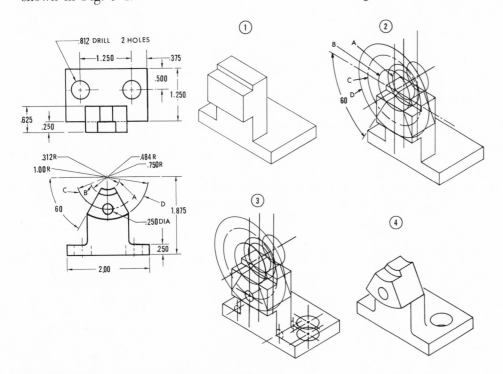

Fig. 9-3 Rectangular-center-line construction.

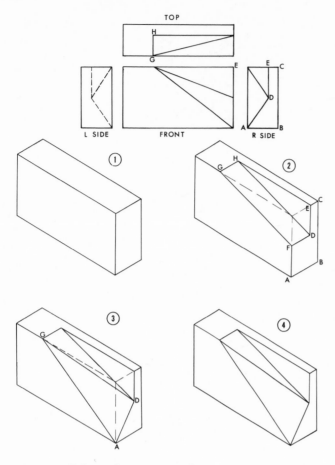

Fig. 9-4 Oblique-plane construction.

CENTER-LINE LAYOUT

The center-line layout involves the location of center lines for holes, semicircles, arcs, fillets, and rounds, as indicated in Fig. 9-5. It normally does not require any boxing-in construction. This layout varies from the cylindrical layout in that with center line there are usually irregular shapes that must be drawn and tangents to arcs and curves. This type of layout requires the accurate use of ellipse templates, and this is its main characteristic.

CYLINDRICAL LAYOUT

A cylindrical-type layout (Fig. 9-6) requires the use of basic center lines or axes for the cylinders and the placement of ellipses on these center lines. It also requires the proper construction of tangent lines to the ellipses. The cylindrical layout may require a section view as shown in this illustration.

CONICAL LAYOUT

The accurate use of ellipse templates is required in conical layouts, as shown in Fig. 9-7. Center lines are required for the accurate drawing of ellipses or

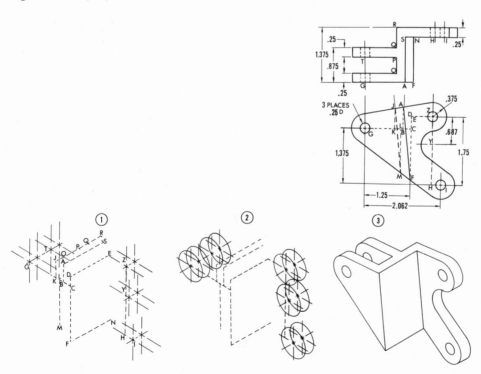

Fig. 9-5 Center-line construction.

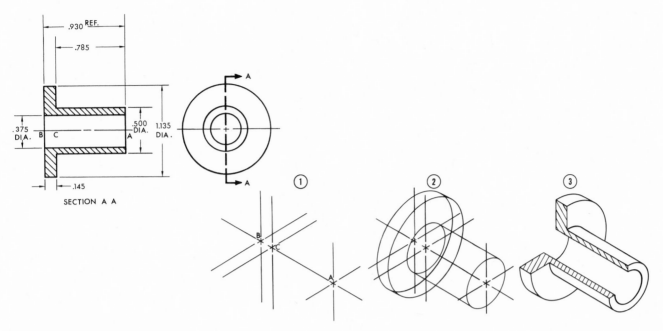

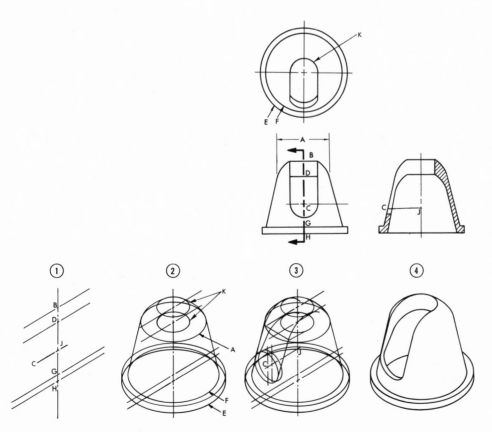

Fig. 9-6 Cylindrical construction.

Fig. 9-7 Conical construction.

parts of an ellipse. The important point in drawing a conical shape is to locate the point of tangency of a curve with a straight line as indicated on the orthographic view, distance *A*. In many cases it is necessary to locate the outer surface of a cone, such as in this example.

SPHERICAL LAYOUT

In three-dimensional drawing, a sphere is represented by a circle. In the case of an isometric sphere, be sure to draw the circle $1\frac{1}{4}$ times the indicated diameter, since isometric drawings are about $1\frac{1}{4}$ times larger than the true. Many times in drawing spherical objects, it is necessary to locate points on the outside of the sphere or to draw only a partial sphere (see Chap. 5). This requires the accurate use of ellipse templates as well as the location of angles on the sphere. An example of this is shown in Figs. 9-8 and 9-9.

SECTIONAL LAYOUT

Sectional layouts require the cutting away of parts of a cylindrical object or rectangular parts including sheet metal. (See Chap. 5.) Occasionally a partial section or broken-out section is made to reveal some important detail which would otherwise be hidden. Sections of cylindrical objects should have the cutting plane along one of the axes of the illustration. The cross-hatching used on sections should be at a different angle from the axis of the illustration. Be sure to use a different angle for the horizontal surface than

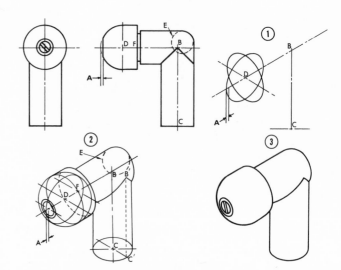

Fig. 9-9   Spherical construction.

for a vertical surface in a half section; otherwise, distortion will result. See Fig. 9-10*b* for an example of a half section. More detailed information for sections is given in Chap. 5.

PHANTOM LAYOUT

Phantom-line layout can be used with advantage, especially when parts are to be shown within an outer housing.

Phantom lines are used instead of solid lines to give the impression of looking through glass. This type of layout is shown in Fig. 9-10*a*.

Phantom-line layouts are sometimes substituted for section layouts, especially when interior parts are to remain assembled.

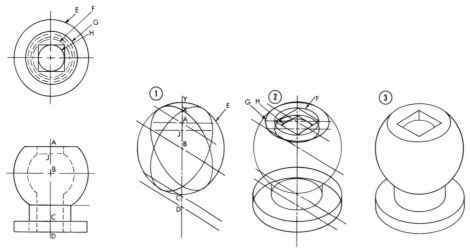

Fig. 9-8   Spherical construction.

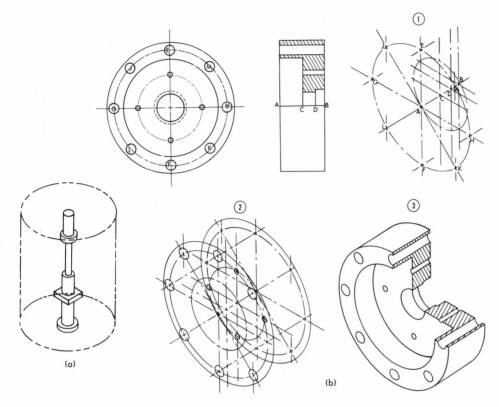

Fig. 9-10 (a) Phantom layout. (b) Section construction.

IRREGULAR SHAPES

Irregular shapes require that compound angles be plotted in most cases. Given random points are determined on the orthographic drawings, and these same points are then plotted on the illustration. This type of layout usually involves the use of the center-line and boxing-in methods, as shown in Fig. 9-11.

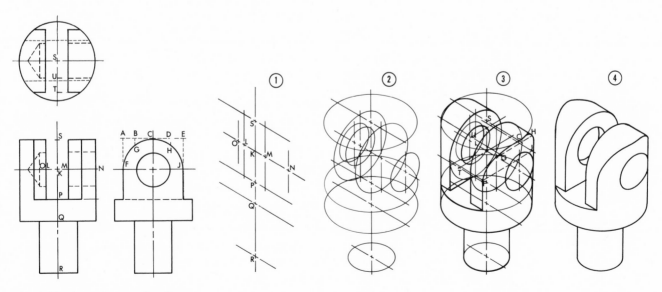

Fig. 9-11 Irregular construction.

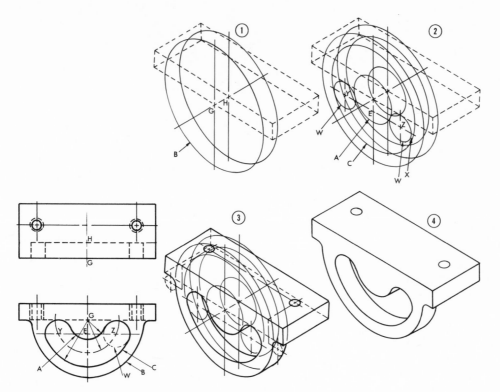

Fig. 9-12 Construction with ellipse.

ELLIPSE LAYOUT

Figure 9-12 shows a layout where the ellipse has a special function. It also illustrates an oddity of the ellipse which requires some adjustment, as illustrated in Chap. 4. The ellipse is used in almost every layout; however, there are layouts like this one where the ellipse plays a major role. Notice that at point x in step 2 an ellipse problem presents itself. The ellipse to represent the lower part of the slot does not touch the tangent point of the small ellipse which determines the width of the slot. The larger ellipse must be moved slightly to become tangent to the smaller ellipse. This move is necessary because the major-axis distance and the minor-axis distance of an ellipse are not proportional. This problem is illustrated in Chap. 3.

GEAR LAYOUT

Gears may be constructed by means of a circle-projection method, using the orthographic views and projecting points to ellipses (see Fig. 9-13). The ellipses represent the diameter of the circles. This is an isometric illustration of a gear, and, therefore, the added step in view 3 must be used. Ellipse J is an isometric ellipse with an indicated diameter equal to the diameter of the orthographic view. Since isometric is about $1\frac{1}{4}$ times larger than a true representation, this extra step is required. In the case of a dimetric, trimetric, or perspective illustration, this extra step is not required. For isometric, then, the points located in step 2 must be projected to ellipse J, step 3, to obtain the proper isometric size. Notice that the teeth appear wider at the minor-axis point of the ellipse.

The Lietz isometric ellipse protractor (see Chap. 6) can be used to construct a gear if the illustration is isometric. The angle between the teeth may be determined and then marked off by using the protractor (Fig. 9-14). The orthographic view of a gear is shown with the necessary construction lines added. This construction is duplicated in the isometric view. Tangent lines are drawn from the ellipse B to the angle points of the teeth, D, E, F, G, H, J, K, and L, in order to obtain the teeth shape. This is another example of using the ellipse as a measuring device. (See Chap. 7.)

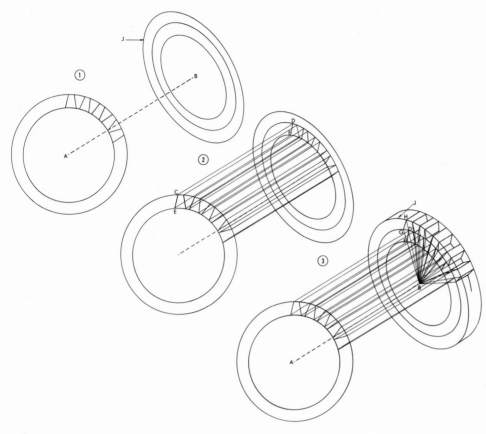

Fig. 9-13 Gear construction.

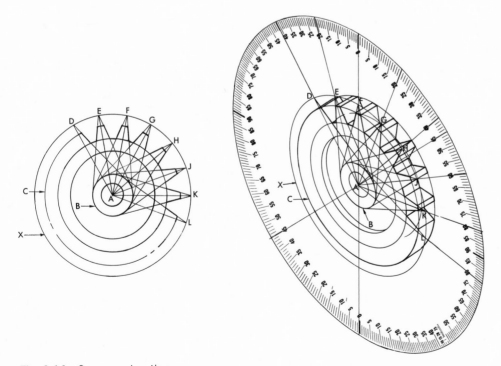

Fig. 9-14 Gear construction.

To layout a dimetric, trimetric, or perspective gear, you may use the above techniques, but obtain the angle of the teeth by using a circle-projection method (Chap. 7) or a dimetric or trimetric protractor (Chap. 11). The ellipse at C, B, and X would, of course, be the proper angle ellipses instead of the isometric ellipses.

Boxing in for Gear Construction. The boxing-in method may be used for constructing a gear. This method is illustrated in Fig. 9-15, which shows the orthographic view of a partial gear with coordinate points established. These same points can be transferred to the isometric box by dividers. The intersection of line EF with line BF and the intersection of line DG with CG locate the gear teeth.

Gear Grids. Some gear grids are available but with limited sizes and number of teeth.

Simplified Gears. Gears are sometimes shown in a simplified manner, especially if they are small, as in Fig. 9-16.

Worm-gear Layout. A worm-gear layout is shown in Fig. 9-17. The orthographic view is given with the isometric solution. After the center line is drawn, lines are drawn to indicate the diameter A of the gear, and a cylinder is formed. The amount of pitch and the angle are laid out on the cylinder as indicated. An angle ellipse is selected, in this case 25°, which is placed so that the major axis is aligned with the angle line. The diameter of the ellipse would be the diameter that would fit within the exterior lines of the cylinder. The root of the teeth B is drawn, and the same angle-size ellipse is used to complete the root lines as is used for the crest lines.

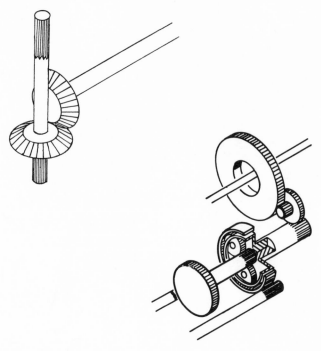

Fig. 9-16 Simplified gear construction.

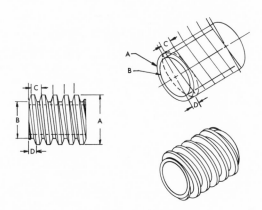

Fig. 9-17 Worm-gear construction.

PIPE LAYOUT

Pipe layout is explained and illustrated in Chaps. 5 to 7; it involves the use of ellipse templates, angle measurement, and intersections, and requires solving for the proper angle-size ellipse on inclined planes.

PLACEMENT OF PARTS AND FLOW LINES

Several methods are used for the placement of parts on an exploded illustration: the parts may partially overlap, be completely separated, or be partially assembled. In many cases all three methods are combined.

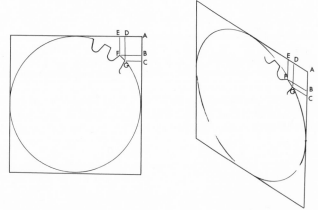

Fig. 9-15 Gear construction—boxing in.

One basic point should be kept in mind when locating exploded parts on an illustration: Never hide an important characteristic of a part by covering it with another part. In most cases, parts may overlap other parts if no detail is obscured; however, there are some occasions when an illustrator is expected to explode parts so that there is no overlapping. Given specifications often determine the method to follow.

When parts are exploded from their assembly point, a line is drawn like the one in views *B* and *D*, Fig. 9-18. This line is called a *flow line, center line, explosion line,* or *sequence line.* The most frequently used term is flow line. The line is usually shown as a conventional center line or as a dashed line. In some cases a thin solid line is used for a flow line.

Flow lines are normally placed parallel to the vertical or horizontal axis of the illustration (Fig. 9-19).

Overlapping Parts. View *A*, Fig. 9-18, shows the two bolts overlapping the main part and covering not more than half of the holes. No flow lines are

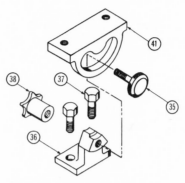

Fig. 9-19 Flowline construction.

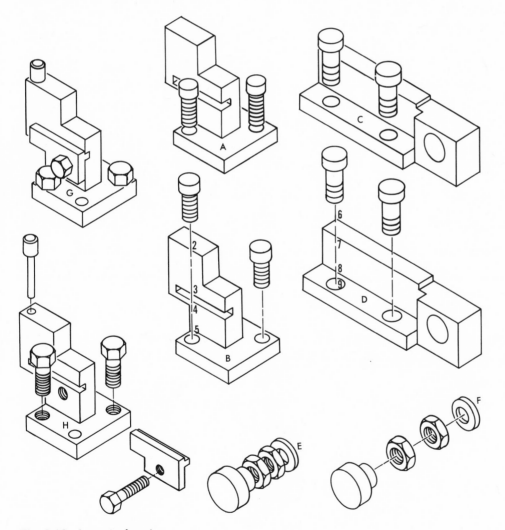

Fig. 9-18 Layout of parts.

used since obviously they are not necessary. There are short breaks in the lines that appear behind the bolts. In some companies, however, these breaks are not used. View C shows the bolts exploded but not overlapping the holes as in view A. No flow lines are used in view C since it is clear that the bolts assemble in the holes shown. In views B and D the bolts are exploded completely off the main object, and it is necessary to use flow lines.

When flow lines cross object lines, a break is shown in the object lines crossed. See views B and D. In some cases the break is shown on both sides of the flow line as at 2, 3, 4, and 5. In other cases the break is shown only on one side of the flow line, such as in view D at points 6, 7, 8, and 9. View E shows overlapping of parts with not more than half of the hole covered. Do not show a part just touching the edge of another part. The same parts completely exploded are shown in view F. Notice that the flow lines go only to the center of the holes, and that, in this case, the object lines are broken on both sides of the flow lines. Some illustration groups show flow lines covering the complete hole if other parts are exploded on the other side. Flow lines are placed parallel to the axis of the illustration. When it is necessary to change the direction of flow lines, a three-dimensional, $90°$ angle is used (see Fig. 9-19). This corner may be square or curved.

LEADERS AND INDEX NUMBERS

In most exploded illustrations, parts are identified by means of an index number or a letter located at the end of a leader (see Fig. 9-20). Techniques vary widely; however, listed below are some typical examples. Leaders and index numbers are usually placed on an illustration by means of paste-up material, which has an adhesive coating on one side that will stick to the illustration's surface. There is also a type of paste-up material which can be placed on the illustration by merely rubbing lightly over the numbers, letters, or symbols with a ball-point pen or pencil. This type of paste-up cannot be moved in case of a change or error, and if removal is necessary, it must be scraped off. The sticky-back type can be removed and placed in a different location, although it takes more time than the rub-on type. Special

typewriters are sometimes used to make index numbers and callouts on opaque paper with a sticky back (Avery paper) or on paper without a sticky back (Rely). With the latter the paper is attached using a waxing machine or rubber cement. There are other methods; however, the above are the most commonly used.

Leaders and index numbers or letters are sometimes placed on a clear acetate covering over the illustration instead of on the illustration itself. This method makes it easier to make changes in the illustration and reduces the possibility of damaging the illustration's surface or smearing adhesive material.

Index numbers are repeated if the parts are the same and separated. If duplicate parts adjoin, they may be shown by one leader for each part or, better still, by leaders extending from the duplicate parts to the same index number.

Assignment of index numbers is usually according to the order of assembly of parts, as shown in Fig. 9-20. In some cases the sequence of numbers follows in a clockwise manner. Avoid crossing leaders and flow lines as well as other parts.

Leaders are usually straight lines, although some have a short shoulder next to the number. Occasionally it is necessary to show a jog in the leader to avoid another leader or number. Be sure the

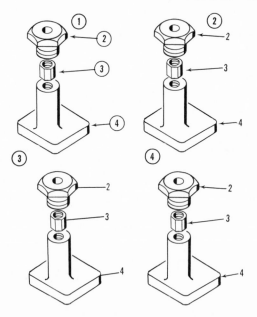

Fig. 9-20 Index numbers and leaders.

leader extends from the center of the index number and not from one side. (See Fig. 9-20.)

Four common examples of leaders are shown in views 1, 2, 3, and 4, Fig. 9-20. In view 1 a leader is shown with an arrow that does not quite touch the object. In view 2 a leader is shown with an arrow not touching the object and the index number without a bubble. In view 3 a leader is shown without an arrow and just touching the edge of the object. View 4 shows the arrow on the leader just touching the object. Sometimes the end of the leader is placed on the surface of the object and occasionally leaders are shown as slightly curved lines. When a leader must cross an object line, a paste-up material is used with a white border on the black leader line. This white border may be on only one side or on both sides of the leader. When this arrangement is photographed, it shows as a break in the object lines where the leader crosses.

When leaders cross object lines, care should be taken that the leader is not paralled to an object line, since confusion may result in determining whether the leader is part of an object line. Leaders are normally placed in a general horizontal, diagonal, or vertical position, although they do not have to be parallel to each other. It is suggested that the leaders be placed in an orderly manner so that the angle between the object line and the leader is not less than 45°. The length of the leader depends on the layout of the illustration and amount of reduction in size. The leader should be neither too long nor too short. Proper spacing of index numbers should be maintained, and this spacing may govern the length of the leader and also determine if the leader should have a jog. Index numbers should be located in line wherever possible, as shown in Fig. 9-21.

SPOT DETAILS

Technical illustrations are sometimes made as assembly-type illustrations with spot details of exploded subassemblies. Spot details are used to show revolved views (Fig. 9-22). They also show separate parts exploded and enclosed by a complete or partial circle (Fig. 9-23), a bracket (Fig. 9-23), or a rectangle (Fig. 9-23). When the circle is used, an index letter appears, as at *A*. Frequently a large black arrow is used at *A* on the assembly instead of a line as indicated here. A spot enlargement is used when the object is too small to be identified, as in Fig. 9-24.

PROPORTIONAL DIVIDERS

A proportional divider is a valuable instrument which speeds up the work of the technical illustrator when he is making a layout. It is a necessary tool for one who wishes to be successful in this field. It permits the illustrator to measure lines at a given ratio, to divide lines into any given number of parts, to divide the circumference of a circle into a given

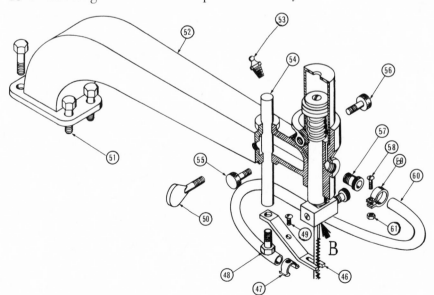
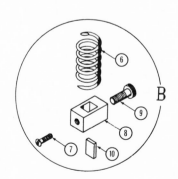

Fig. 9-21 Placement of leaders.

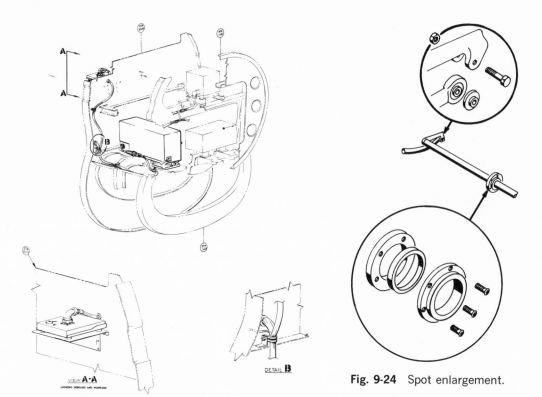

VIEW **A·A**
LOOKING INBOARD AND FORWARD

DETAIL **B**

Fig. 9-22 Revolved views.

Fig. 9-24 Spot enlargement.

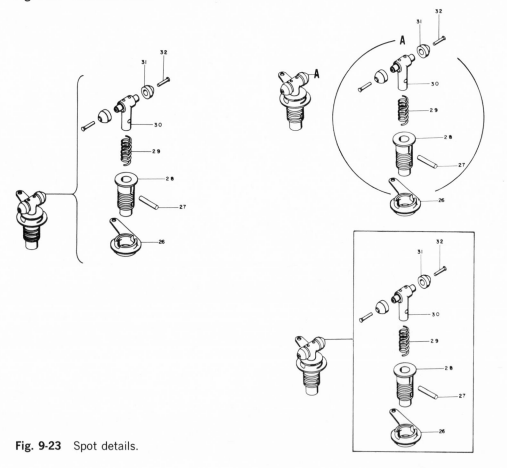

Fig. 9-23 Spot details.

number of parts, and to enlarge or reduce the size of circles. In many cases, when drawing from blueprints, illustrators use proportional dividers to scale directly from blueprints and to enlarge, reduce, or draw to actual size. Instead of reading the dimensions from the blueprint and then using a scale to measure the dimension, they use the divider.

The proportional divider is composed of two legs attached with an adjustable pivot. The pivot can be moved to a desired scale marked on the legs, thereby permitting the user to obtain a proportion between one end of the divider and the other.

One side of the leg is marked *circle*, and the other side is marked *lines*. In view *A*, Fig. 9-25, the divider is set so that the distance between the points on one end is twice the distance between the points on the other end. This is possible, as the spot enlargement shows, because the index mark is set opposite the number 2 on the lines side. By scaling the blueprint with the end marked *E*, one can double the dimensions, as shown by 2*E* at the other end. By scaling the blueprint with end marked 2*E*, one can reduce the dimension by $\frac{1}{2}$, as shown by *E* at the other end. Any proportion can be obtained, and, as indicated in view *B*, the distance between the

points on one end is 4 times the distance between the points on the other end. This proportion is obtained by setting the index line opposite the number 4 as illustrated by the spot enlargement. By setting the index line on the "lines" side opposite a given number, one can divide lines into equal parts or lengthen them to any given proportion.

In view *A*, a line can be divided into two equal parts by setting the 2*E* end to the total length of the line and using the other end *E* to divide the line. In view *B*, a line can be divided into four equal parts by setting the index line opposite the number 4.

The circumference of a circle can be divided into any number of equal parts, view *C*, Fig. 9-25, if the index line is set opposite the desired number on the side marked "circle" and the points of the dividers at *A* are set to the diameter of the circle. In this example, by setting the *A* distance to the diameter of a circle, the circumference can be divided into six equal parts, using distance *B*. Some dividers have the circle scale marked so that the radius is used instead of the diameter. The circle scale cannot be used for dividing an ellipse.

The dividers can be used for dimetric or trimetric illustrations if the proper foreshortening of dimensions

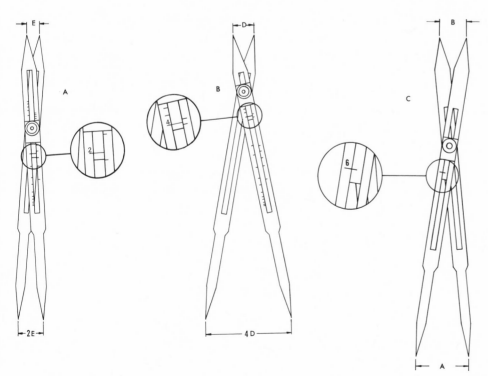

Fig. 9-25 Proportional divider use.

is found and an index line then scratched on the slide which gives the desired foreshortening.

There are many other uses of proportional dividers for draftsman, but most of them do not apply directly to technical illustration, except in the cases shown in views *A* and *B*.

COMMERCIAL PASTE-UP MATERIAL

Numerous printed aids are used in technical illustration for shading and lettering and for making special symbols, numbers, dimensions, and even complete parts such as fasteners. An unlimited number of items are available as timesaving methods for completing an illustration. (See Fig. 9-26.) One type has an adhesive back which sticks to the illustration and another which is pressure sensitive is applied by being rubbed on the backing sheet with a pencil or ball-point pen.

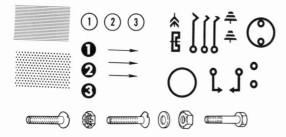

ARTIST-AID

JAY G. LISSNER • 3417 W. 1st ST., LOS ANGELES 4, CALIF.

Fig. 9-26 Commercial paste-up material.

STANDARD PARTS

Many standard parts are called out by means of a number and letters instead of a detail drawing on blueprints. This letter and number designation can be found in bound volumes which give the size, shape, and specifications of the part. The parts are indicated by a military abbreviation as follows: MS, military specifications; NAF, Naval aircraft factory; AN, Army Navy; NAS, national aircraft standards; and AND, Army Navy design.

Questions

1. Define layout.
2. What is of primary importance in making a layout?
3. Describe the procedure for boxing in.
4. Name several layout patterns for technical illustration.
5. Describe two methods for drawing a gear.
6. What basic point should be kept in mind when locating exploded parts on an illustration?
7. What are flow lines? Give another name for these lines.
8. What is an index number?
9. Give three examples of leaders.
10. Explain how leaders are drawn.
11. What is a spot detail? Give three examples.
12. What is the use of a spot enlargement?
13. Explain how to divide a line into four equal parts with the proportional dividers.
14. Explain how to divide the circumference of a circle into four equal parts with the proportional dividers.

PROBLEMS: GROUP 7
Pipe Layouts

Draw isometric illustrations of the pipe T, the elbow, and the 45° fitting.

The isometric ellipse protractor can be used to draw the 45°. Obtain the length of the 45° pipe by using the ellipse as a measuring device. You can obtain the proper angle size for the 45° pipe, using the isometric ellipse protractor. Remember to use the diameter of the angle-size ellipse, $1\frac{1}{4}$ times the indicated diameter on the blueprint.

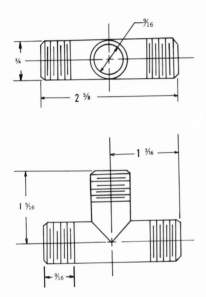

Prob. 7-1 Pipe T.

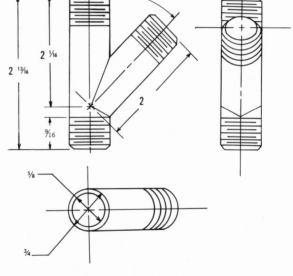

Prob. 7-2 Pipe 45.

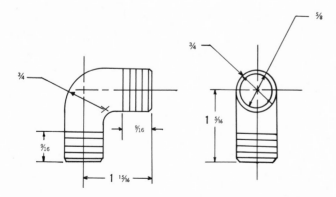

Prob. 7-3 Pipe elbow.

PROBLEMS: GROUP 8
Gear Layouts

Draw isometric illustrations of the gears, using the
three methods explained in the chapter.

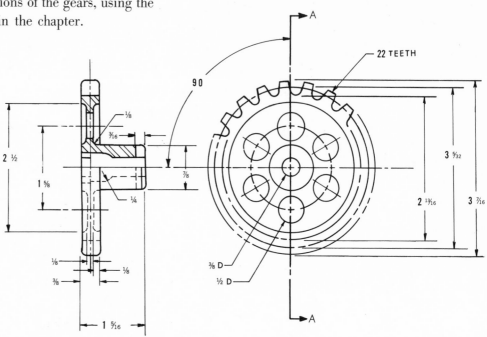

Prob. 8-1 Spur gear.

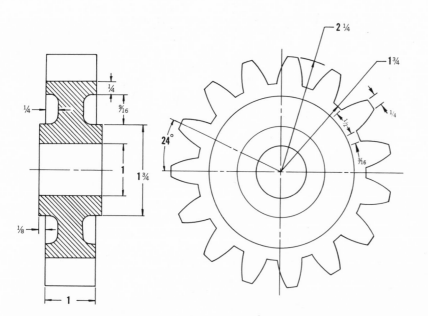

Prob. 8-2 Spur gear.

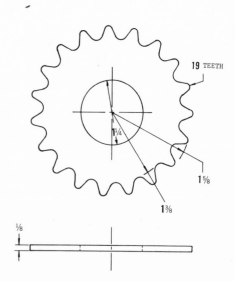

Prob. 8-3 Ratchet gear.

PROBLEMS: GROUP 9
Irregular Shapes—Advanced Problems

Most of these problems require the use of all the techniques explained in previous chapters. Draw these problems in isometric. They can be drawn in dimetric, trimetric, and perspective after these chapters have been studied.

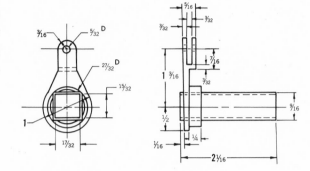

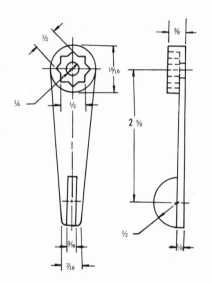

Prob. 9-1 Adjustment handle.

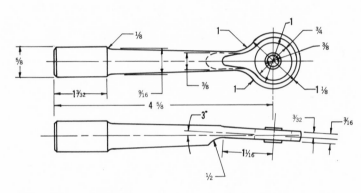

Prob. 9-2 Clevis shaft.

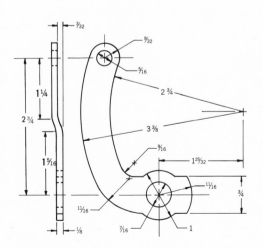

Prob. 9-3 Crank.

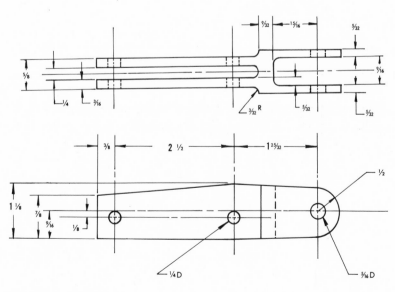

Prob. 9-4 Slotted arm.

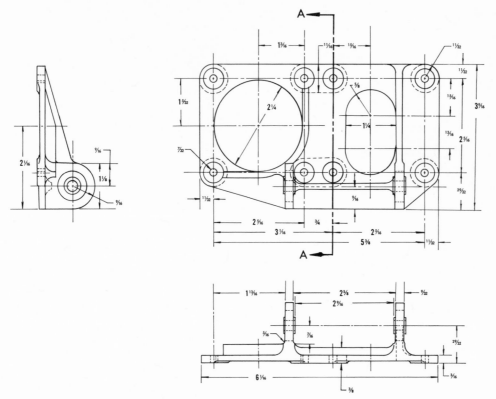

Prob. 9-5 Base lug.

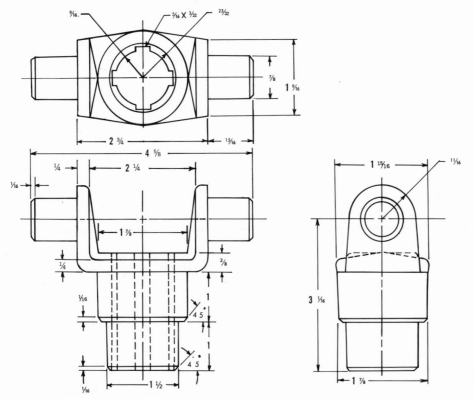

Prob. 9-6 Universal.

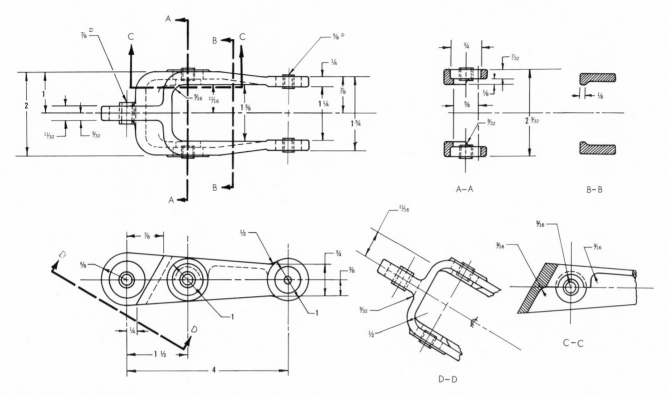

Prob. 9-7 Clevis fork.

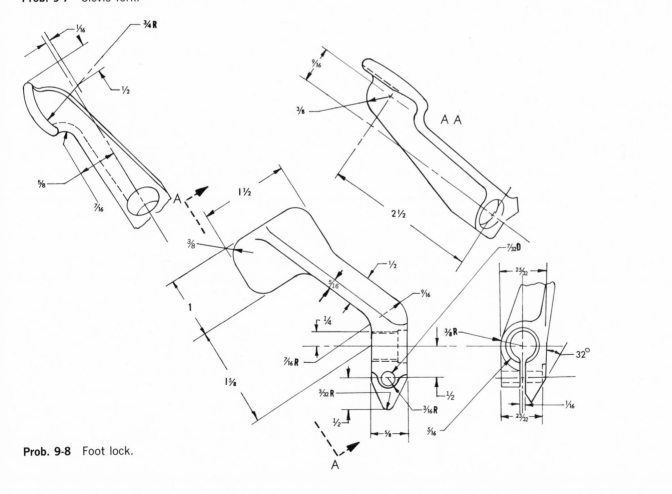

Prob. 9-8 Foot lock.

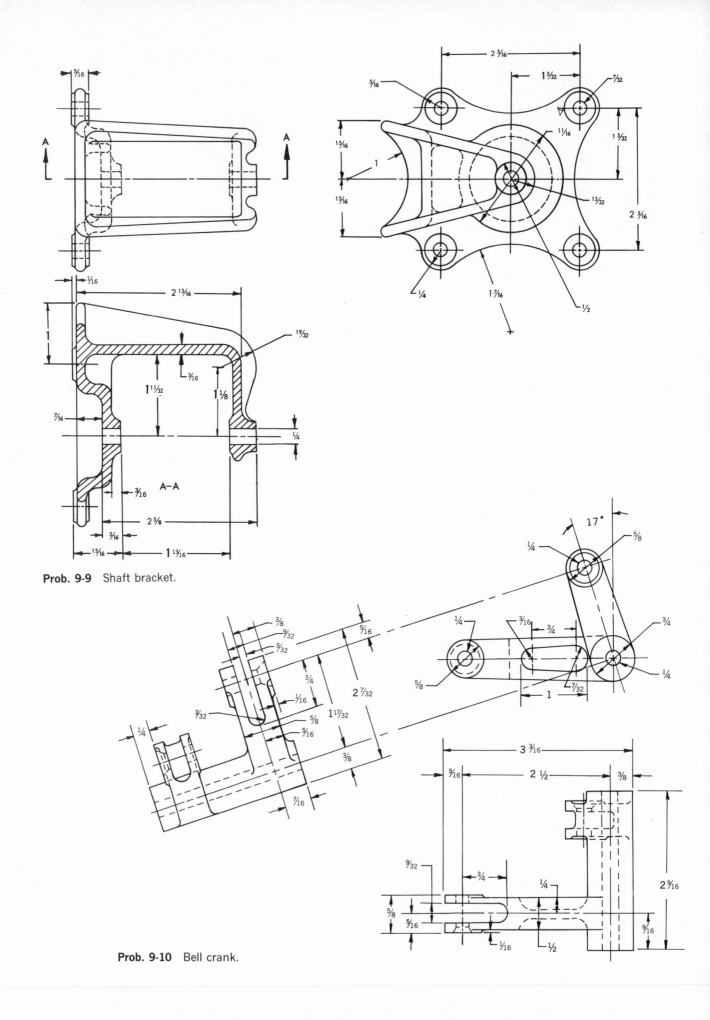

Prob. 9-9 Shaft bracket.

Prob. 9-10 Bell crank.

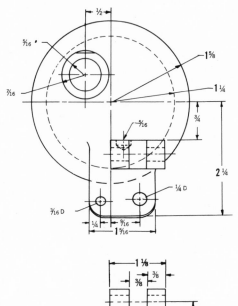

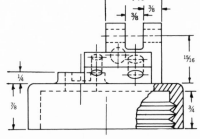

Prob. 9-11 Angle cap.

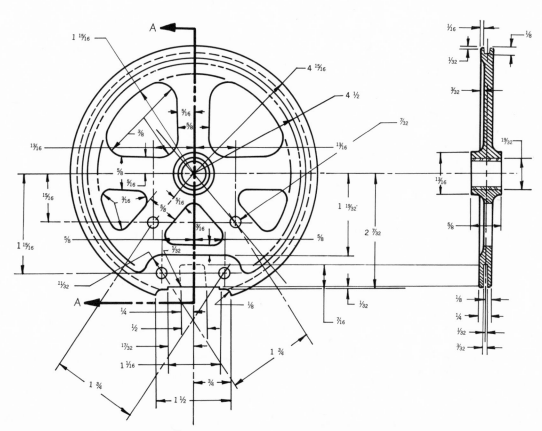

Prob. 9-12 Cable wheel.

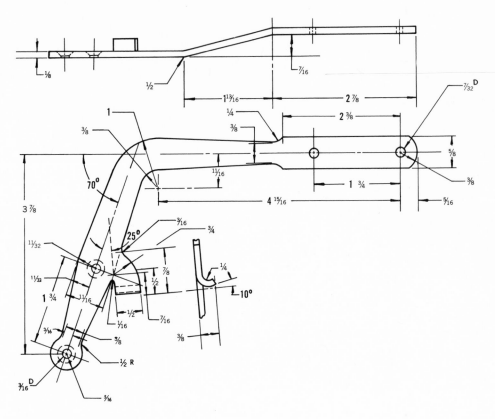

Prob. 9-13 Offset handle.

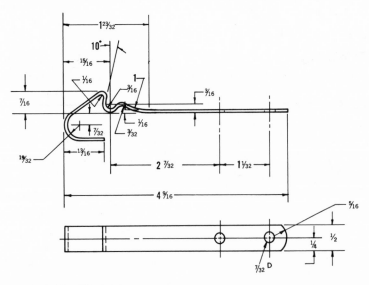

Prob. 9-14 Clip latch.

10 PERSPECTIVE DRAWING

A perspective drawing is a three-dimensional drawing that shows an object as the eye sees it from one particular point. In this respect perspective drawing is like a photograph of an object.

There are several major differences between the method for constructing a perspective drawing and the methods used for other types of drawings previously discussed. One of the main differences is that parallel lines are not drawn parallel as they are in other methods. In perspective, parallel lines converge and, if extended, will intersect at a vanishing point. Another major difference is that there is no scale that can be used for measuring in perspective other than on a mechanical aid such as the Andersen or Klok perspective board or the perspective grid.

A perspective drawing is the best method for representing an object in three-dimensional drawing. Unfortunately, however, to make a mechanical perspective drawing of an object without mechanical aids requires too much time and is seldom done in industrial technical illustration.

Several mechanical aids have been devised, however, which make it quite simple to draw in perspective. These devices eliminate the usual time-consuming and awkward preliminary work required for making a perspective drawing. For example, the proper scales are shown, and the axes are predetermined on the Andersen or Klok perspective drawing board and perspective grid. This timesaving method of perspective drawing is much used in industry.

Because of the limited use of the conventional perspective drawing in industrial technical illustration, most of the discussion in this chapter is of the mechanical aids and grids used in perspective.

There is an unlimited number of methods for making perspective drawings, but all of them adhere to a few basic principles. The technical illustrator should be familiar with these fundamentals in order to understand the theory of perspective and make proper use of perspective drawing aids.

PERSPECTIVE TERMINOLOGY

An understanding of terminology used in perspective is important in discussing the fundamentals.

The *picture plane* is an imaginary plane similar

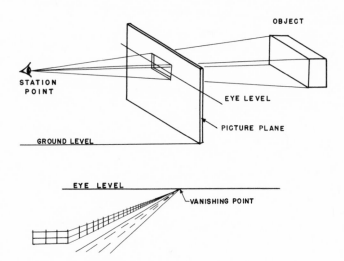

Fig. 10-1 Perspective terms.

to a pane of glass upon which lines of sight from the object form an outline of the object, as in Fig. 10-1.

The *eye level*, or *horizon line*, is a line which is on a level with the observer's eye, as shown in Fig. 10-1. A top view of an object is obtained by drawing the object in a position below eye level. A bottom view of an object is obtained by drawing the object in a position above the eye level.

The *station point* is the position of the observer or the point of observation (see Fig. 10-1). The *vanishing point* is a point at which parallel lines seem to converge, as shown in Fig. 10-1. This effect of convergence may be observed when you look down a road. The sides of the road appear to come together in the distance. The point at which they seem to meet is the vanishing point.

TYPES OF PERSPECTIVE

There are three types of perspective: one-point, or parallel; two-point, or angular; and three-point, or oblique. They are illustrated in Figs. 10-2 to 10-4, which show a cube above and below the eye level.

Two basic systems are used for mechanical construction of a perspective drawing: the plan-view method and the measuring-line method. Most technical illustrators use a combination of both systems if an illustration is made using mechanical perspective.

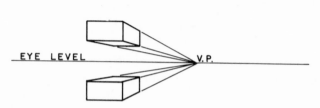

Fig. 10-2   One-point perspective.

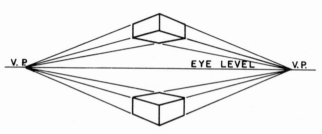

Fig. 10-3   Two-point perspective.

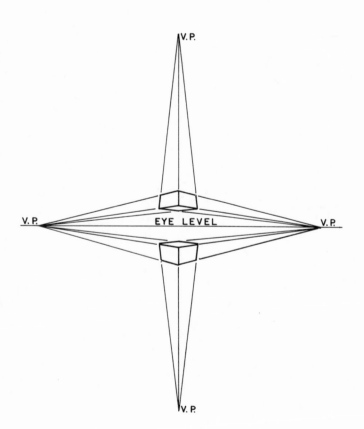

Fig. 10-4   Three-point perspective.

ONE-POINT PERSPECTIVE: PLAN-VIEW METHOD

A simple one-point perspective problem is illustrated in Fig. 10-5 and is constructed mechanically in the following manner with the plan-view method. In the plan-view method, depth measurements are obtained by projecting lines from the plan view to the station point.

1. Establish the eye level or horizon line. The location of this point is arbitrary and depends on whether the object is to be pictured above or below the eye level.
2. Locate the picture-plane line. Draw it near the top of the paper so that it is not in the way of the drawing. The picture-plane line may be the same line as the eye-level or horizon line.
3. Draw the plan view on the picture-plane line. The plan view may be placed above or below the picture-plane line; however, it is easier to draw it resting on the picture-plane line.
4. Draw the ground line—the arbitrary position below the picture-plane line and parallel to it. The location of the ground line depends on how far below the eye level you wish to place the object.
5. Locate the station point. Place this point at a distance of at least twice the width of the object or two or three times its greatest length from the nearest point of the plan view. Distortion will result if it is placed any closer. The station point may be located directly in front of the plan view; however, locating it at one side is better in most cases.

6. Project the width of the plan view to the ground line.
7. Draw the front view of the object on the ground line. This will be true size if the front of the plan view is touching the picture plane. If the plan view is behind the picture-plane line, the front view of the object will be smaller. If the plan view is ahead of the picture-plane line, the front view of the object will be larger than true size.
8. Project a vertical line from the station point to the eye level. This point on the eye-level line will be the vanishing point.
9. From corners C and D of the front view, draw lines to the vanishing point.
10. Project a line from point A on the plan view to the station point. From point K where this line crosses the picture-plane line draw a vertical line downward to the intersection at B and E. This will give the depth of the object and locate the back corners.
11. The height of the object is measured on the front plane, as at CD.

ONE-POINT PERSPECTIVE: MEASURING-LINE METHOD

The measuring-line method for one-point perspective is illustrated in Fig. 10-6. The result is the same as that obtained in the plan-view method. Instead of being obtained by projection from a plan view, depth measurements are laid off along the measuring line, and these points are projected to a measuring point on the eye level. The measuring-line method eliminates the use of the plan view but requires the location of a measuring point on the eye-level line.

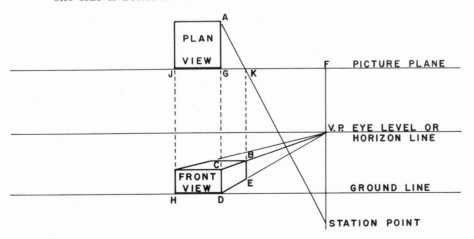

Fig. 10-5 Plan-view method —one point.

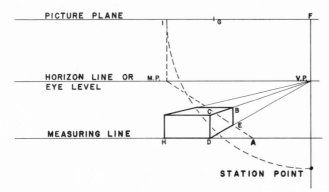

Fig. 10-6 Measuring-line method—one-point.

The following steps are used in the measuring-line method:

1. Establish the eye level.
2. Locate the picture plane as in the plan-view method. The picture-plane line may be the same as the eye-level line.
3. Draw the ground line as in the plan-view method. This line is also used as the measuring line.
4. Locate the station point in the same manner as in the plan-view method.
5. Place point *G* on the picture-plane line the proper distance from the station point. This distance should be same as that shown in plan-view method.
6. Project point *G* vertically downward to the measuring line.
7. Measure distance *HD* equal to the width of object.
8. Project a vertical line from station point to horizon line. This point on the horizon line will be the vanishing point. Continue this line to the picture-plane line, locating point *F*.
9. Locate measuring point. With *F* as center and a radius equal to the distance from *F* to the station point, swing an arc to the picture-plane line at point *I*. Draw a vertical line from *I* to the eye level, or horizon line. This is the measuring point *MP* on the horizon line.
10. Draw a line from point *D* to the vanishing point. Measure the depth of the cube *DA* along measuring line.
11. Draw a line from *A* to *MP*. The depth of the object is at point *E*, the point at which this line crosses the line drawn from *D* to the vanishing point.

12. The height of the object is measured on the front plane at *CD*.
13. Complete the object as shown.

The picture-plane line may be located on the same line as the horizon line. They have been shown separately here in order to explain more fully the terminology of perspective.

TWO-POINT PERSPECTIVE: PLAN-VIEW METHOD

The procedure for drawing two-point perspective using the plan-view method is illustrated in Fig. 10-7. Two orthographic views of the object are also shown. The following are the steps used to draw this object using the plan-view method:

1. Establish the eye-level line or horizon line.
2. Draw the picture-plane line. Place it near the top of the paper so that it is out of the way of the drawing.
3. Draw vertical line *O-SP* and place station point at *SP*. Point *O* represents the nearest corner of the object. Remember to place the station point at a distance of at least twice the total width of the object from point *O*. In this case, this distance would be about twice distance *G*, as shown in Fig. 10-7.
4. Draw the plan view of the object in the desired position with the nearest corner at *O*. In this drawing, one side of the object is drawn at an angle of 30° with the horizontal and the other side at 60° with the horizontal. Other angles commonly used are 15 and 75°, and 45 and 45°. The side of the object with the most detail is usually placed along the axis with the smallest angle, because more of the surface can be seen along this axis.
5. Draw line from *SP* to 1. This line is drawn parallel to side *OP* of the object.
6. Draw vertical line from 1 to *VPR*, locating vanishing point right.
7. Draw line from *SP* to 2 parallel to side *OR* of the object. Angle *A* formed by *SP*-1 and *SP*-2 is always 90°. Lines *SP*-1 and *SP*-2 may be drawn at various angles with the horizontal as long as angle *A* is equal to 90°. Lines *SP*-1 and *SP*-2 must be parallel to the sides of the plan view, however.

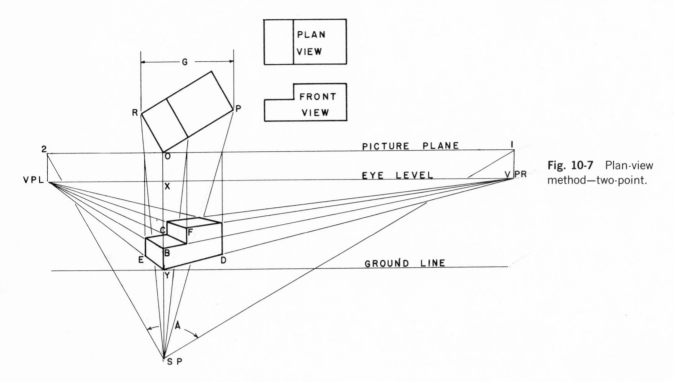

Fig. 10-7 Plan-view method—two-point.

8. Draw a vertical line from 2 to *VPL*, locating vanishing point left.
9. Draw lines from plan view corners *R*, *P*, and *O* to station point *SP*.
10. Project vertical lines downward from the point at which these lines intersect the picture-plane line to intersect *Y-VPR* and *Y-VPL* at points *D*, *Y*, and *E*.
11. All vertical measurements, *YC* for total height and *YB* for height of notch, are made along *YX* and then projected to *VPR*.

TWO-POINT PERSPECTIVE: MEASURING-LINE METHOD

Following are the steps used in the measuring-line method as shown in Fig. 10-8.

1. Establish the eye-level line or horizon line.
2. Draw the picture-plane line. Place it near the top of the paper so that it is out of the way of the drawing.
3. Draw vertical line *O-SP* and place the station point at *SP*. Point *O* represents the nearest corner of the object. Remember to place the station point at a distance of at least twice the total width of the object from point *O*—in this case, at least twice distance *G* shown in Fig. 10-7.

4. Draw a line from *SP* to 1. This line is drawn parallel to one side of the object. In this case it is drawn at 30° with the horizontal.
5. Draw a vertical line from 1 to *VPR*, locating vanishing point right.
6. Draw a line from *SP* to 2. In this case it is 60° with the horizontal since angle *A* must be 90°.
7. Draw a vertical line from 2 to *VPL*, locating vanishing point left.
8. With 1 as center and radius equal to 1-*SP*, locate 3. Draw a vertical line from here to eye level, locating measuring point left *MPL*. With 2 as center and radius equal to 2-*SP*, locate 4. Draw vertical line from here to eye level, locating measuring point right *MPR*.
9. Locate the nearest corner of the object at *Y* on vertical line *O-SP*. *Y* is the desired distance below the eye level. Of course this point may be placed above the eye level, depending upon what view of the object is desired.
10. Draw a horizontal measuring line through point *Y*. Draw a line from *Y* to *VPR* and from *Y* to *VPL*.
11. Mark off depth measurement *Y-B*, width measurement *Y-C*, and depth of notch *Y-J* on measuring line.

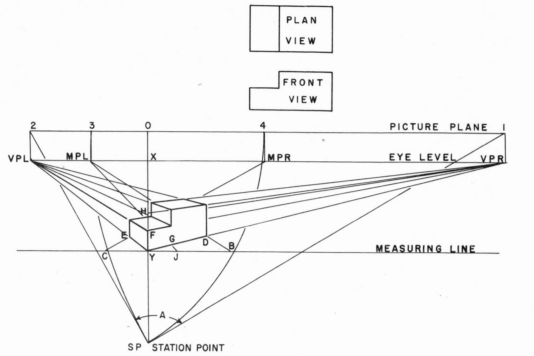

Fig. 10-8 Measuring-line method—two-point.

12. From point *B* draw a line to *MPL*, locating depth measurement at *D*.
13. From point *C* draw a line to *MPR*, locating width measurement at *E*.
14. From point *J* draw a line to *MPL*, locating depth of notch at *G*.
15. All vertical measurements are made on line *X-Y*, beginning at *Y*. *Y-H* is total height of object, and *Y-F* is height of notch.
16. Complete the object as shown.

ANDERSEN PERSPECTIVE DRAWING BOARD

The Andersen perspective drawing board is a mechanical aid which is used extensively in making perspective drawings. There are two types of boards: the two-point board and the three-point board.

Drawings made on the Andersen board can be quickly drawn to photographic accuracy. Time is an important factor in technical illustration, and the Andersen board is a timesaving device that makes it possible for even those with limited knowledge of perspective to prepare perspective drawings of any type.

The Andersen perspective drawing board and centrolineal T square are shown in Fig. 10-9. The drawing board is edged with three arcs, and the surface is imprinted with three corresponding meas-

uring lines which cross one another at the *focal point*. The lines are scaled in units of measure which diminish toward the vanishing points. Each of the three arcs is centered upon the vanishing point of its corresponding measuring line. From these lines, the shape of an object in three dimensions can be plotted. One line measures all vertical distances on the object to be drawn; the remaining two lines measure the two horizontal distances, width and depth. A specially designed T square with two bearing surfaces to ride along the arcs automatically takes care of the convergence of lines to the vanishing points.

The Measuring Lines. The three measuring lines at right angles to one another *represent* the intersection of the three planes. The measuring lines may be thought of as three rulers suspended in space

Fig. 10-9 Andersen drawing board. The perspective drawing board and the centrolineal T square. (G. Andersen.)

at right angles to each other. Each line extends toward its vanishing point in the direction indicated in Fig. 10-10. When starting to project a drawing, you should locate the center point of intersection (focal point) in the middle of the object or at some convenient reference point near the middle. The focal point is always used as a starting point from which dimensions of the object are taken.

Selection of Views. A wide selection of views of an object may be obtained, as shown in Fig. 10-11. The drawing board may be placed, with respect to the illustrator, in any one of six positions, as shown in Fig. 10-12.

When starting a projection, the first step is to select that position of the board which will show to best advantage the object to be drawn. By rotating Fig. 10-12, you can select any one of the six views of the cube. To look sharply down on the object, place the arc with the shortest radius on the board directly in front of the illustrator's chest (position 1). The other two arcs (positions 3 and 5) give views from varying heights above the object. To look up at the object, place one of the flat edges of the board (position 2, 4, or 6) in front of the chest. Whichever way the board is placed, the line that is perpendicular to the illustrator is the vertical measuring line, or height line. The other two lines then measure the horizontal dimensions, width and depth. If the object faces the illustrator's right, the depth line is the one which extends toward the left arc. In each case the remaining horizontal line will be the width line.

The board is so designed that each of the three measuring lines has a different degree of foreshortening with respect to the observer. The illustrator may

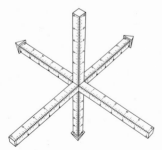

Fig. 10-10 Measuring system—Andersen drawing board. Measuring lines on the board may be thought of as three rulers suspended in space at right angles to one another. (G. Andersen.)

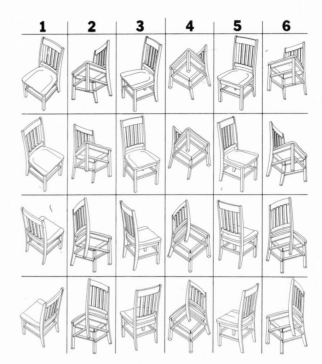

Fig. 10-11 Selection of views on Andersen board. The six positions of the board will produce these twenty-four different views of the object. (G. Andersen.)

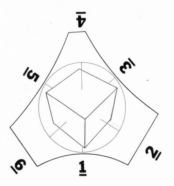

Fig. 10-12 Andersen board positions. The drawing board positions. The drawing board may be placed, with respect to the draftsman, in any one of these six positions. (G. Andersen.)

place the board in any one of the six positions indicated in Fig. 10-12 according to the view desired. These six positions produce 24 different views as shown in Fig. 10-11, and by reversing these drawings you obtain 24 additional views, which are, of course, opposite views. The units of measurement on the board may represent inches, feet, or any other distance on the object which will result in a drawing of desired size. Figures 10-13 and 10-14 are examples of drawings prepared on the Andersen board.

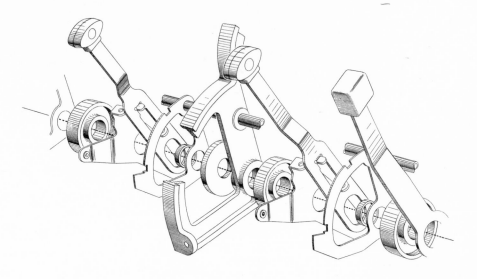

Fig. 10-13 Drawn on Andersen board. (G. Andersen.)

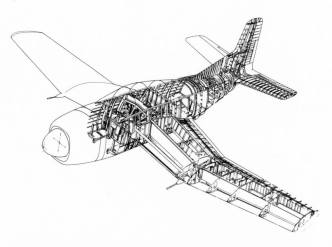

Fig. 10-14 Drawn on Andersen board. (G. Andersen.)

Sketching on the Andersen Board. The drawing board may be used as a guide for making freehand sketches. The direction of the perspective planes of the sketch should follow the direction of the three measuring lines. The object, roughly sketched for general shape and proportion, can be cleaned up and its perspective accuracy guaranteed if you use the T square in conjunction with the arcs.

Drawing the Problem. The drawing of simple problems with the board is illustrated in Figs. 10-15 and 10-16. Proceed as follows:

1. Select the position of the board that will show the best view of the object. Position 3 was selected in Fig. 10-12.
2. Determine the scale to use.

3. Locate the position of the object on the board. The middle of the object should be located on the focal point or as near it as is conveniently possible.
4. The side elevation (Fig. 10-15*b*) is scaled in two dimensions, then plotted on the two corresponding measuring lines on the board showing height and depth.
5. The front elevation (Fig. 10-15*c*) is scaled in two dimensions, height and width, and then transferred to the corresponding measuring lines on the board.
6. The plan view (Fig. 10-15*d*) is scaled in two dimensions and then plotted on the corresponding horizontal measuring lines of the board to show depth and width.
7. The ellipse from the plan view in Fig. 10-15*d* is projected upward to coincide with its positions in the front and side elevation projections. In Fig. 10-15*e*, contour lines are added to complete the drawing. Figure 10-16 shows the drawing of another problem using the Andersen board.

INDUSTRY-DESIGNED GRIDS

Several industrial companies have designed their own perspective grids, which do not give complete accuracy but rather approximate measurements. These measurements are satisfactory for eyeballing a view of an object. An example of a perspective grid appears in Fig. 10-17. These grids are limited to one specific view of an object, and exact scales are

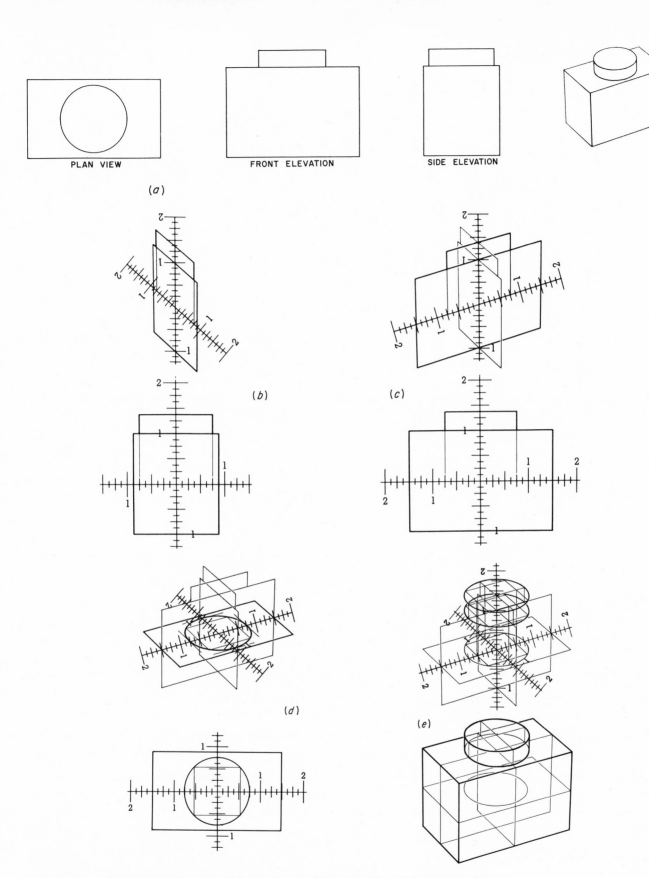

PLAN VIEW FRONT ELEVATION SIDE ELEVATION

(a)

(b)

(c)

(d)

(e)

Fig. 10-15 Solution of problem on Andersen board: (a) perspective and corresponding three-view orthographic drawings of an ink bottle, (b) side elevation, (c) front elevation, (d) plan view scaled in two dimensions, (e) ellipse from the plan view projected upward to coincide with its positions in the front and side elevation projections: contour lines are added to complete the drawing. (G. Andersen.)

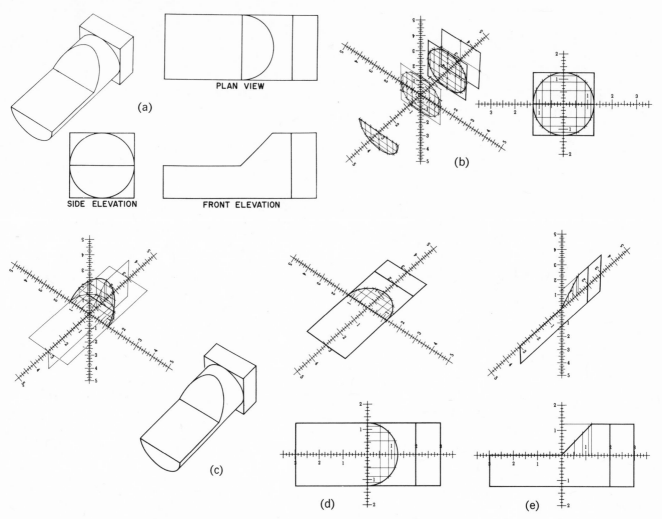

Fig. 10-16 Solution of problem on Andersen board. (*a*) Perspective and corresponding three-view drawings of an abstract form. (*b*) The front view is scaled in its dimensions, width and height, and then transferred to the corresponding measuring lines on the board, where it is projected both forward and backward on the depth line as a series of cross sections located at three critical positions on the object. (*c*) A canted curve is plotted by series of rectangular measurements from the plan and side views (top). The finishing contours are added and construction lines removed. (*d*) The plan view is scaled in two dimensions and then plotted on the corresponding horizontal measuring lines. (*e*) The side view is scaled in its two dimensions, depth and height, and then transferred to the board. (G. Andersen.)

not shown on the grid. An example of the Andersen board being used in the construction of a three-dimensional view of an airplane is shown in Fig. 10-18.

ANDERSEN PERSPECTIVE CHART

The Andersen three-point perspective chart is used in much the same way as the board (Fig. 10-19). It contains the three measuring scales as the board

does and grid lines which converge to vanishing points. The grid lines on the chart function like the centrolineal T square on the board. These grid lines are yellow lines which can easily be seen and yet which do not cause confusion with the lines of the drawing. Even light pencil lines overlying the yellow grid lines can easily be recognized and not be lost or confused with the grid lines. By using the same methods as with the board, one may change

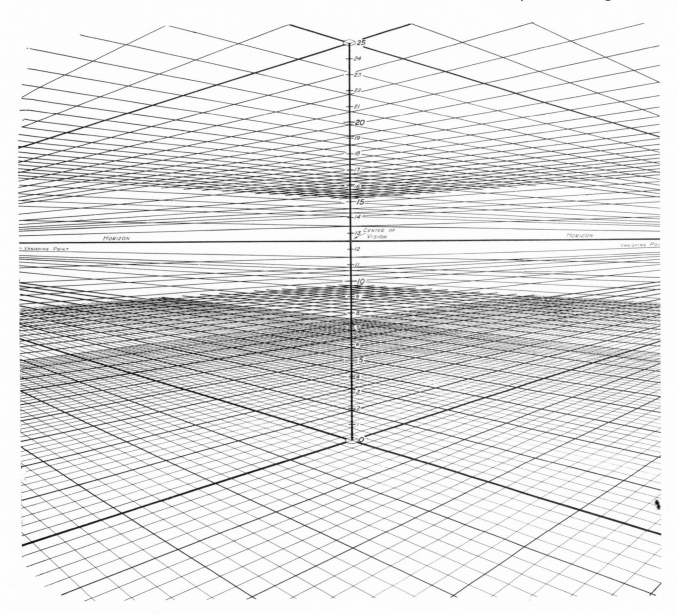

Fig. 10-17 Perspective grid. (North American Aviation, Inc.)

the position of the chart to obtain various views of an object. This chart or grid is used extensively in industry.

PERSPECTIVE MEASUREMENTS WITH DIAGONALS

A practical method for measuring in perspective utilizes diagonals, as illustrated in Fig. 10-20. Diagonal lines *AC* and *BG* are drawn to divide the surface *ABCG* into two equal parts. Line *KL* is drawn to the vanishing point through the intersection point of lines *AC* and *BG*. This operation makes

lines *AK*, *KG*, *BL*, and *LC* represent equal distances in perspective. To find the center of surface *APNG*, draw diagonal line *AN* and locate the center where this line intersects line *KL*. The center of surface *GJHE* is located by the intersection point of lines *GH* and *EJ*. Lines *GJ*, *JN*, *NO*, *OR*, and *RS* represent equal perspective distances. Distance *NO* is determined by drawing diagonal line *MO* through the intersection point of lines *PN* and *KL*. The other distances are obtained in like manner with the indicated diagonal lines.

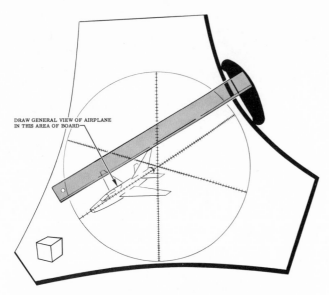

Fig. 10-18 Drawing aircraft on Andersen board. (North American Aviation, Inc.)

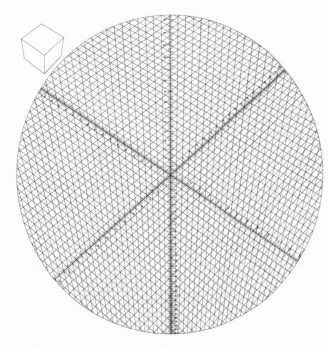

Fig. 10-19 Three-point perspective grid.

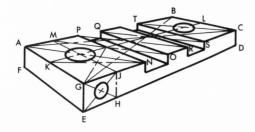

Fig. 10-20 Diagonal perspective measurement.

PERSPECTIVE ELLIPSES

One of the problems in perspective drawing is the solution for the proper angle-size ellipse. An explanation for this solution is given in Fig. 10-21. As illustrated the ellipse diameter size becomes smaller and the angle size becomes larger as lines converge at the vanishing points.

Perspective squares can be drawn, and an ellipse can be fitted so that it circumscribes the square with the minor axis aligned with the vanishing line. This is a practical solution which is adequate, although not entirely theoretically correct.

The theory of perspective ellipses is vividly shown in Fig. 10-22. This is a photograph of a box with circles of equal diameter spaced equal distances apart. The circles appear as ellipses, and the diameter size and the angle size of the ellipses decrease in size toward the vanishing point.

KLOK PERSPECTIVE DRAWING BOARD

The Klok perspective drawing board (Fig. 10-23) is a valuable timesaving device for making accurate perspective drawings. The special T square and scales on the board eliminate the usual tedious work involved. Examples of drawings made on this board are shown in Fig. 10-24.

Questions

1. Define perspective drawing.
2. What is the main difference between perspective drawing and methods previously discussed?
3. Define picture plane, eye level, station point, and vanishing point.
4. Name three types of perspective.
5. Describe the plan-view method.
6. Describe the measuring-line method.
7. What mechanical aid is widely used to make perspective drawings?
8. Why is mechanical perspective seldom used in technical illustration?
9. Where would you place an object in perspective if the bottom surface were to be shown?
10. What is the main disadvantage of mechanical perspective in technical illustration? Advantage?
11. Is it possible to use a scale when drawing in perspective?

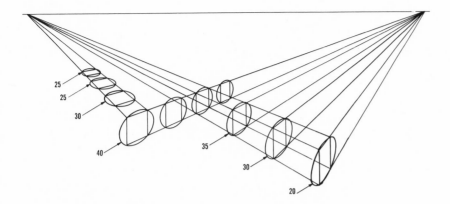

Fig. 10-21 Perspective ellipse size.

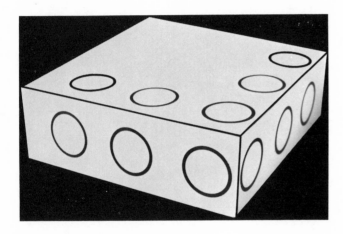

Fig. 10-22 Photograph of circles.

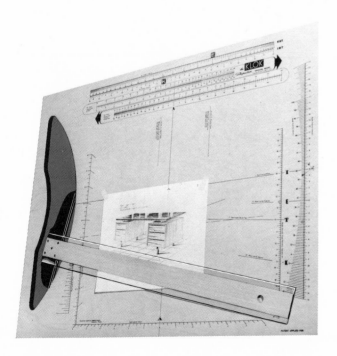

Fig. 10-23 Klok perspective board. (John H. Klok.)

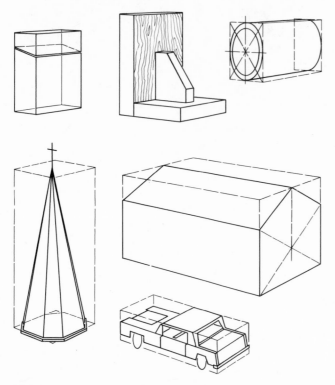

Fig. 10-24   Drawings on Klok perspective board.   (John H. Klok.)

Exercises

Select problems from group 1, Chap. 3 and draw in perspective using the plan-view and measuring-line methods.

Use the perspective grid to draw several basic problems from Group 1. Draw problems using each of the six different positions of the grid. After the basic operation of the grid is mastered, draw an assembly from Group 10 in the back of the book. The layout of parts must be carefully planned, because the parts cannot be moved to a different position on the finished drawing. This would upset the perspective and cause distortion.

Draw some of the problems on the Andersen board and on the Klok perspective drawing board.

Practice drawing ellipses using the inscribed-square method described in the chapter.

11

DIMETRIC AND TRIMETRIC DRAWING

DIMETRIC DRAWING

A dimetric drawing is a three-dimensional drawing in which two of the axes make equal angles with the plane of projection. Two of the angles between the three axes are equal (see Fig. 11-1). Two foreshortened scales are needed in dimetric drawing. In Figs. 11-1, 11-3, and 11-4, measurements along axes *AO* and *OB* are made with the same foreshortened scale, and measurements along axis *OC* are made with another foreshortened scale. In Fig. 11-2 measurements along axes *AO* and *OC* are made with the same scale, and measurements along *OB* are made with a different scale.

In Figs. 11-1, 11-3, and 11-4, the same angle ellipse is used on surface *AOCX* and surface *COBZ*, because the angle between the axes is the same on these surfaces. A different angle ellipse is used on surface *AOBY*. In Fig. 11-2, the same angle ellipse is used on surfaces *AYBO* and *COBZ*. (See Fig. 11-9, view 1.)

The most common type of dimetric drawing is made

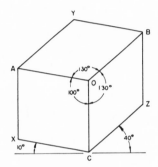

Fig. 11-2 Dimetric.

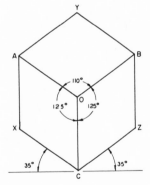

Fig. 11-3 Dimetric.

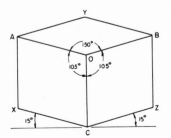

Fig. 11-1 Dimetric.

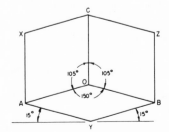

Fig. 11-4 Reversed-axis dimetric.

with the two receding axes drawn at 15° from the horizontal (see Figs. 11-1 and 11-4). The same foreshortened scale is used along these two axes, and the vertical measurements are made with another foreshortened scale. In some places true scale is used on the vertical axis.

Other angles may be used for the receding axes in dimetric drawing as long as two, and only two, of the angles between the three axes are equal and more than 90°.

The dimetric axis to be selected depends upon what view of the object is desired. The 35°–35° axis will show the greatest amount of the top of an object (Fig. 11-3). The 15°–15° axis gives the maximum view of the vertical surfaces and the minimum view of the top (see Fig. 11-1). The 10° − 40° axis gives a view that is a compromise between the views seen with the other two axes. These axes may be reversed, just as in isometric and oblique, to show the bottom view of an object, as in Fig. 11-4.

TRIMETRIC DRAWING

A trimetric drawing is a three-dimensional drawing in which the three axes make different angles with the plane of projection. The angles between the three axes are all different sizes, as shown in Fig. 11-5. Three different scales are needed, one for each of the three axes. These scales are all foreshortened and change whenever the angles between the axes change. A different angle-size ellipse is needed for each surface.

Trimetric drawings are seldom made in industry mainly because of the inconvenience of using a different scale for measurements along each axis. Some of the most common trimetric axes used are 15°–45° and 25°–35° (Fig. 11-6).

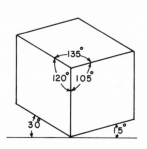 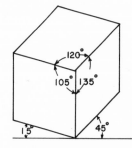

Fig. 11-5 Trimetric.

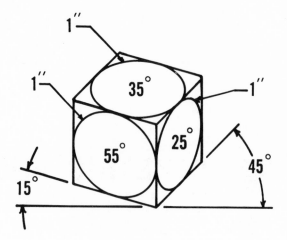

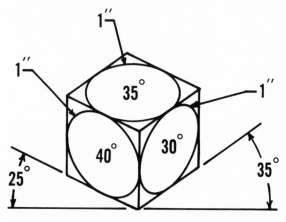

Fig. 11-6 Trimetric ellipse sizes.

SOLVING FOR ANGLE-SIZE ELLIPSE

When using dimetric and trimetric drawings, the first thing you should do is solve for the proper angle-size ellipse to use on the horizontal and vertical planes. This solution is shown step-by-step in Fig. 11-7. To do this graphically, procceed as follows:

1. Select desired axes *AC, CB, CD* (view *a*). Draw line *AB* perpendicular to the vertical axis *CD*. Draw line *BD* perpendicular to axis *AC* and draw line *AD* perpendicular to axis *CB*. Make this drawing large enough to maintain reasonable accuracy. Use an $8\frac{1}{2} \times 11$-in. sheet of paper.

2. In view *b*, find the center of lines *AB, BD,* and *AD*. Draw semicircles as indicated.

3. In view *c*, extend axis *AC* to intersect the semicircle at *E*. Draw lines *BE* and *DE*. Extend axis *CD* to intersect the semicircle at

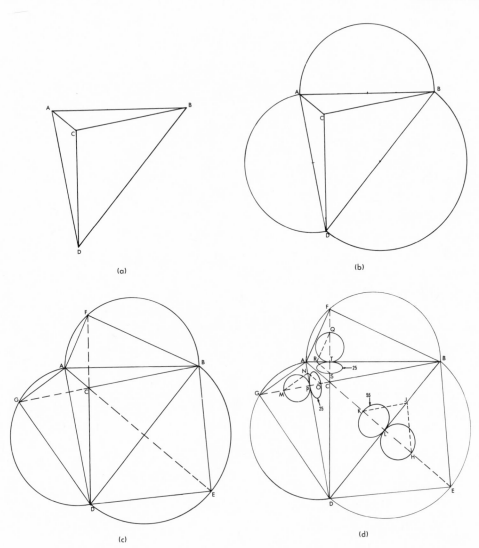

(a)   (b)

(c)   (d)

Fig. 11-7 Finding angle-size ellipse on dimetric or trimetric horizontal or vertical plane.

F. Draw lines *AF* and *BF*. Extend axis *BC* to intersect the semicircle at *G*. Draw lines *AG* and *DG*. Triangle *BED* is the true shape and size of surface *CBD*. Triangle *AFB* is the true shape and size of surface *ABC*. Triangle *ADG* is the true shape and size of surface *ACD*.

4. Draw a circle on surface *BED* (view *d*); make it at least 1″ in diameter for better accuracy. Draw line *HJ* parallel to *BE* and draw line *JK* parallel to line *BC*. Line *KL* represents the distance across the minor axis of the proper ellipse for this surface. Select an angle ellipse which is equal in diameter to the circle and will pass through points *K* and *L* with the minor axis aligned with axis *AC*. In this case the

ellipse is 55°. In some cases no angle ellipse will pass exactly through these points; however, use the ellipse that is the nearest. This will give sufficient accuracy for any illustration.

Use the same procedure for the solution of the other two surfaces. Notice that the ellipse for surfaces *ABC* and *ACD* is the same, 25°, since it is for a dimetric drawing. In other words, two of the surfaces of a dimetric illustration have the same angle-size ellipse, in this case, surface *ABC* and *ACD*. Angles *ACB* and *ACD* are the same; therefore, the angle-size ellipse on these surfaces is the same. Only the solution for one of the surfaces is then needed because the other surface will be the same.

PRACTICAL DIMETRIC AND TRIMETRIC DRAWING

Dimetric and trimetric illustrations in industry do not always follow the strict use of theoretical foreshortened scales, axes, and angle-size ellipses. Variations from the true theoretical do not pose a problem, because for accepted accuracy and for practical technical illustration, they are entirely adequate. The actual theoretical angles for the receding axes are more precise and are usually expressed in degrees and minutes, but for practical purposes and actual use, the angles are usually rounded off to the nearest 5 degrees. Therefore, because of all these factors, a compromise must be made when selecting the ellipses, the scales, and the axes.

ADVANTAGES AND DISADVANTAGES

Dimetric and trimetric illustrations give the advantage of showing an object in many different views with less distortion, and these views give the reader a more accurate picture than does isometric. On the other hand, a disadvantage is the necessity for using two different foreshortened scales for dimetric and three for trimetric as compared with one regular scale for isometric. In addition, two different angle-size ellipses must be used in dimetric, and three different angle-size ellipses in trimetric, on the horizontal and vertical planes. In isometric, only one type of ellipse is used.

REVOLVING THE AXES

Once the receding axes of dimetric or trimetric illustrations are selected, the axes may be revolved in order to give different views without changing the foreshortened scales or the angle-size ellipses. Figures 11-8 to 11-10 show frequently used dimetric drawing axes and illustrate this revolution of axes for obtaining different views. In view 1, Fig. 11-8, AD is the vertical axis, and this axis is revolved in view 2 so that AD is then the left receding axis and the other axes revolved accordingly. The scale on these revolved axes remains the same, and the angle-size ellipses on the revolved surfaces remain the same. The proper 1″ angle-size ellipses appear on the sur-

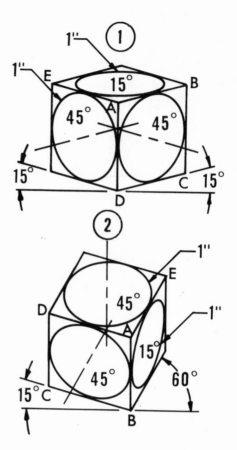

Fig. 11-8   Dimetric rotation axis.

faces for Figs. 11-8 and 11-9. Figure 11-9 shows a 10°–40° dimetric illustration and demonstrates how the axes may be revolved in much the same way as in 11-8. The vertical axis AD in view 1, Fig. 11-9, becomes the left receding axis in view 2. Figure 11-10 shows how a different view of an object can be obtained by revolving the axes. This figure also shows a comparison of the size of the dimetric views with an isometric view.

VARIATIONS IN ANGLE ELLIPSE AND FORESHORTENED SCALE

As mentioned in the preceding section, strict theory is not always followed in establishing the exact axes and foreshortened scales in dimetric and trimetric illustrations. For example, with the frequently used 15°–15° receding axes (Fig. 11-8), the theoretical foreshortened scale along axes AB and AE is slightly less than ¾″ for a full scale illustration; however, many illustrators use the regular ¾ scale. The theoretical foreshortened scale along axes AD is

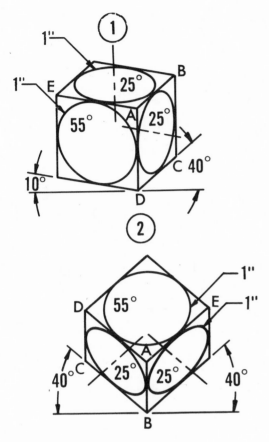

Fig. 11-9 Dimetric rotation of axis.

slightly less than 1″, but again in many cases a regular 1″ scale is used. Some manufacturers have available the theoretical foreshortened scales for this type of dimetric, and these scales are used by some illustration groups.

Variations in angle-size ellipses are used when drawing the 10°–40° receding axes (Fig. 11-9). Some prefer to use the 20 and 60° ellipses on these surfaces instead of the 25°–55°. The theoretical angle-size ellipse may actually be a size between these two variations, but the nearest 5 degree must be used. The variation is not of a serious nature since it is difficult to obtain absolute accuracy using a pencil or pen on an illustration, and furthermore the variation in the shape of ellipses 5° apart is small. It is only the width of a pencil point at the minor axes for up to 1″ in diameter with the major axis the same on all angle-size ellipses for a given diameter. Because of this, most illustration groups consider the accuracy sufficient, regardless of the variation used, as long as the ellipse is to the nearest 5° size.

SCALES FOR DIMETRIC AND TRIMETRIC DRAWINGS

The foreshortened scales for dimetric and trimetric illustrations can easily be obtained by using the ellipse as a measuring device, as discussed in Chap. 7.

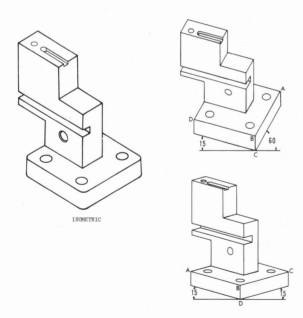

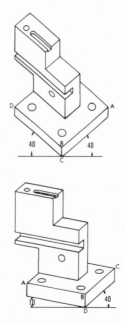

Fig. 11-10 Dimetric views.

When the proper angle-size ellipse is determined for a surface, that ellipse can be used for measurements whether the measurement be along the axis or off axis. In Figs. 11-11 and 11-12, 1″ angle-size ellipses are drawn on the planes with the minor axes aligned properly, perpendicular to the planes. Since these are the proper angle-size ellipses, the lines drawn tangent to the ellipses and parallel to the given axes give the foreshortened scale for a 1″ measurement along the axes. Subdividing the 1″ scales can be accomplished by using different diameter-size ellipses. In dimetric illustrations only one angle-size ellipse is necessary to obtain the two scales. In the 15°–15° dimetric (Fig. 11-11) the 45° ellipse is used to obtain the scales for the vertical axes *BC*, *AD*, and *EF*. The horizontal axes *CD*, *AE*, *AB*, *DF*, and *GB* are also obtained using this same 45° ellipse. Only two

scales are necessary since the scales for the horizontal axes are the same. Three 45° ellipses are drawn with different diameters, and lines are drawn tangent to these ellipses to the vertical axis *BC* and to the horizontal axis *CD* to obtain the fractions indicated. The 1″ foreshortened scales could be obtained with the 1-in. 45° ellipse and then subdivided by geometric construction. The ellipses are used here to show the relation of the ellipses to measuring given distances. The foreshortened scales for the 10°–40° dimetric axes are obtained in the same manner as for the 15°–15°. The foreshortened scales for the vertical axis *AD* is the same as for the horizontal axis *AE*.

After the scales are obtained in this manner, reproductions can easily be made on various materials, or dividers can be used to obtain any given measurement along the axes.

TRIMETRIC SCALES

The technique for determining foreshortened scales in trimetric (Fig. 11-6) is the same as shown in Figs. 11-11 and 11-12 except that two ellipses are needed to obtain the three different scales.

NONDIMETRIC AND NONTRIMETRIC MEASUREMENTS

The ellipse can easily be used for off-axis or inclined-plane measurements as discussed in Chap. 7. All the techniques used in Chap. 7 can be used for dimetric and trimetric illustrations by merely substituting the proper angle-size ellipse for the isometric ellipse.

Dimetric cubes are shown in Fig. 11-13 with three different diameter-size ellipses on the surfaces. The various diameters of these ellipses represent the same

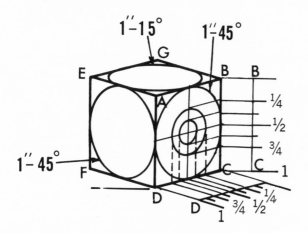

Fig. 11-11 Dimetric scale using ellipse.

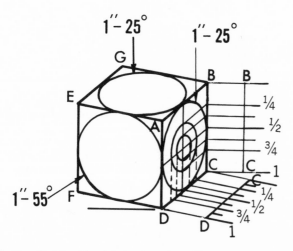

Fig. 11-12 Dimetric scale using ellipse.

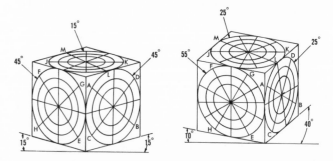

Fig. 11-13 Dimetric measuring with ellipse.

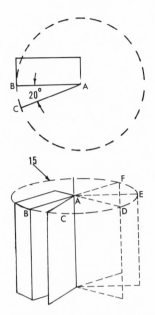

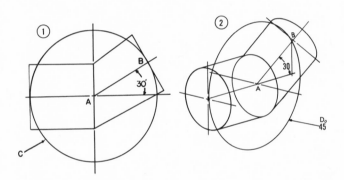

Fig. 11-14 Nondimetric line measuring.

Fig. 11-15 Dimetric measurement with ellipse.

distance regardless of the angle of the line, and the distance can easily be measured by using the proper angle-size ellipse instead of the conventional plotting method.

An example of nondimetric line measurement is shown in Fig. 11-14. This is a 15°–15° dimetric drawing. (See Fig. 11-8, view 1.) The 15° ellipse is used for measurement on the horizontal plane. The technique is the same here as in Chap. 7 on the same object, but the 15° ellipse is used here instead of the isometric ellipse. The 15° ellipse is the same diameter as the circle in the top orthographic view of the box and shows how the length of the box lid is obtained along various nondimetric lines.

Figure 11-15 shows a pipe elbow with the front orthographic view and the dimetric solution for the

length of line *AB* using the ellipse. Because this is for a 15°–15° dimetric illustration, the 45° ellipse is used. The line *AB* is in a vertical plane, and the 45° ellipse is the proper ellipse for the vertical plane. (See Fig. 11-11.) The 45° ellipse *D* is the same diameter as the circle *C* on the front view. The technique for measuring the 30° angle will follow.

MEASURING ANGLES AND OFF-ANGLE ELLIPSES

Measuring angles in dimetric or trimetric by the circle-projection method is shown in Fig. 11-16. This example is the same as the one in Chap. 7, except that the axis and the ellipse are different.

A dimetric problem showing the solution for angles and an angle-size ellipse on an inclined plane is shown in Fig. 11-17. This is a 15°–15° dimetric illustration, and the angle to be measured is in the vertical plane. The 45° ellipse is used since it is the proper angle-size ellipse for the vertical plane of this type of dimetric illustration (see Fig. 11-8, view 1).

Proceed as follows for Fig. 11-17, locating the points in alphabetical sequence.

Step 1. Center a 45° ellipse at *A*. (Use an ellipse at least 2″ in diameter for better accuracy.) Draw the 15° axis *AC* and draw line *AB* along the

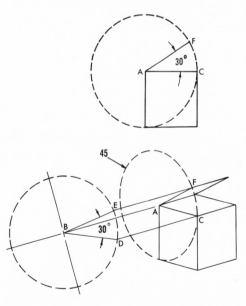

Fig. 11-16 Dimetric angle measurement by circle projection.

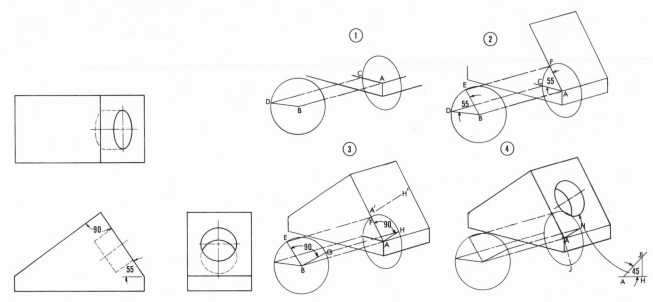

Fig. 11-17 Dimetric angle and angle ellipse size.

other 15° axis. Draw a circle centered at *B* with the same diameter as the ellipse. From point *C*, draw line *CD* parallel to *AB*, locating point *D* on the circle. This is a base line for measuring the 55° angle.

Step 2. Measure the 55° orthographic angle *DBE* on the circle. Project point *E* along a 15° line to *F*. Draw line *AF*.
Angle *CAF* is the 55° dimetric angle.

Step 3. Measure the orthographic 90° angle *GBE*. Project point *G* along a 15° line locating point *H*. Draw line *HA*. Angle *HAF* is a 90° dimetric angle. Line *HA* must be found since this is the axis line for the hole on the inclined plane.

Step 4. Place line *AH* on the base of a right triangle. Construct the perpendicular with indefinite length. Draw *AJ* which is half the major axis of the ellipse. Set a divider to distance *AJ*, and with *A* as center on the triangle strike an arc intersecting the vertical line at *J*. Measure angle *HAJ* on the triangle. This is the proper angle-size ellipse to use for the hole on the inclined plane. The location of the center of the hole can be found by plotting, as previously demonstrated.

For other dimetric or trimetric axes, angles and angle-size ellipses for inclined planes can be solved by following this procedure but with the proper angle-size ellipse substituted for the planes involved.

Some illustration groups have constructed their own protractors. One such protractor is shown in Fig. 11-18. This can easily be accomplished by the circle-projection method. Two different protractors are needed for dimetric and three different protractors for trimetric. Different protractors are needed for each type of dimetric or trimetric illustration.

Two dimetric protractors are shown in Figs. 11-19a and 11-19b. These protractors are for a dimetric drawing with the horizontal axes 15° from the horizontal. (See Fig. 11-8.) Figure 11-19a shows a protractor for the right vertical plane, and Fig. 11-19b shows one for the horizontal plane. The protractor shown in Fig. 11-19a can be used for the left vertical plane if the page is turned over. The numbers on the outside of the protractors indicate the degrees and the numbers inside indicate the proper angle-size ellipse to use at this angle.

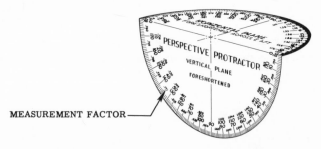

MEASUREMENT FACTOR——

Fig. 11-18 Dimetric protractor (marked perspective). (North American Aviation, Inc.)

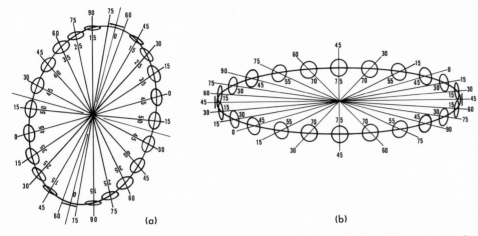

Fig. 11-19 (a) Dimetric protractor for 15°–15° vertical plane. (b) Dimetric protractor for 15°–15° horizontal plane.

Two dimetric protractors are shown in Fig. 11-20 for a dimetric drawing with one horizontal axis 10° from the horizontal and the other 40° from the horizontal. The protractor for the horizontal plane is also used for the right vertical plane.

DIMETRIC SOLUTION OF PROBLEM

The complete solution for a 15°–15° dimetric problem is given in Fig. 11-21. This problem requires the solution for the dimetric horizontal and vertical scales, the measurements for the nondimetric lines and surfaces, and the solution for the angles and the angle-size ellipses on the inclined planes.

Using the ellipse as a measuring device is particularly effective in an exploded illustration such as this,

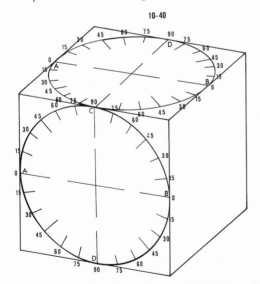

Fig. 11-20 Dimetric protractor 10°–40° angle.

as indicated in Chap. 7. Follow the circle-projection method locating points in alphabetical order.

The inclined plane on the base part is 65° from the vertical. This angle could be measured with a protractor that could be constructed using the circle projection just discussed. The axis *ST* perpendicular to the inclined plane is solved by *AD*, and the proper angle-size ellipse for the inclined plane, 30°, by the triangle *ADE*. Several examples are shown using the ellipse to measure. The line measurements can be determined on the inclined plane by using the 30° ellipse as illustrated or by the 45° ellipses. The diameter size of the 30° and the 45° ellipses would be equal to the distance on the orthographic view. If *MO* is 2″, use a 2-in. 30° ellipse with the minor axis aligned with *ST*. If the bracket thickness is $\frac{5}{16}$″, use the 45°, $\frac{5}{16}$-in. ellipse as shown with the minor axis aligned with *KN*. These are variations of techniques that can be used when the proper angle-size ellipse is known for a surface. Use the technique that appeals to you. Of course all the measurements can be obtained from the large 2-in. 45° ellipse showing all the diameters at the proper angles. A scale for the horizontal and vertical distances is shown and was obtained from the large 2-in. 45° ellipse.

NONDIMETRIC MEASUREMENTS

A simplified circle-projection method can also be used for measuring dimetric angles, angle-size ellipses and length of lines (Fig. 11-22).

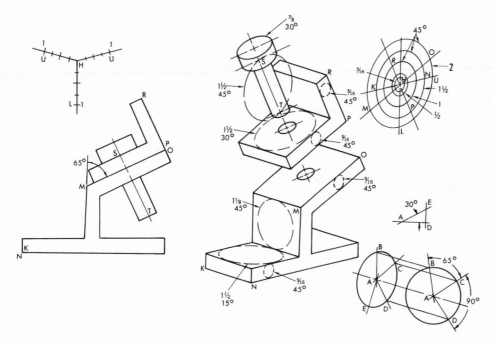

Fig. 11-21   Dimetric solution of angles, angle-size ellipse, and length of lines.

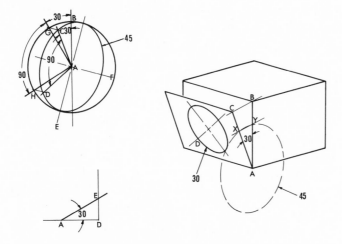

Fig. 11-22   Dimetric simplified solutions.

The circle is superimposed on the proper angle-size ellipse instead of being placed separate from the ellipse, in the same manner as shown in Chap. 7. This is a 15°–15° dimetric problem. The objective is to find angle *BAC*, the proper length of line *AC*, and the proper angle-size ellipse on the inclined plane. The following is the procedure for this solution.

1. Center the 45° ellipse at *A*. Use the 45° since this is the proper angle size to use for the vertical plane.

2. Superimpose the circle on the large 45° ellipse.
3. Measure the 30° angle *BAG* on the circle with a regular protractor.
4. Draw line *GC* from point *G* parallel to *AF* locating *C* on the ellipse.
5. Draw line *CA*, Angle *BAC* is the 30° dimetric angle.
6. Draw line *CA* on the box parallel to the *CA* on the ellipse.
7. Place a 45° angle ellipse on the box, and draw *XY* through points on ellipse where line *AB* and *AC* cross the ellipse.
8. From point *B*, draw *BC* parallel to *XY* to locate the proper length of *CA*. If a large diameter-size ellipse is available that would pass through point *B* when centered at *A*, the lines *XY* and *CB* would not be necessary to locate the proper length of line *AC*.
9. To find the axis for the ellipse on the box lid, measure the 90° on the circle *GAH*; then draw line *HD* parallel to *AF* to obtain the 90° dimetric angle *CAD*.
10. Draw line *DA* to obtain the minor axis for the ellipse on the box lid.
11. To determine the angle-size ellipse for the box lid, measure *AD* from the large ellipse and place on the base of triangle *ADE*. Construct

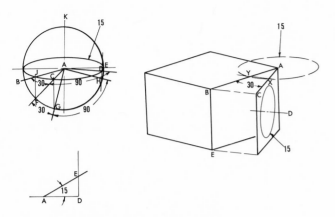

Fig. 11-23   Dimetric simplified solutions.

a perpendicular to *AD*.   Measure *AE* half the major axis of the ellipse, and with center *A* on triangle lay off *AE*.

12.   Measure angle *DAE* 30° on triangle.   Thirty degrees is the proper angle-size ellipse for the box lid.   Align the minor axis of the 30° ellipse parallel with *DA* on the large ellipse.

Figure 11-23 is similar to the above except in the horizontal plane, and the procedure is the same except that the large 15° ellipse is used since this is the proper angle-size ellipse for the horizontal plane of a 15°–15° dimetric illustration.

1.   Draw the circle and the 15° ellipse centered at *A*.

2.   From point *J*, where the ellipse crosses axis *AB*, draw vertical line *JF* locating point *F*, and draw *FA*, the base line for measuring the 30° angle *FAG* on the circle.   Draw line *GC* to get the 30° dimetric angle *JAC*.

3.   Draw line *AC* on the box lid parallel to *AC* on the ellipse.

4.   Measure the 90° *GAH* on the circle; then draw line *HD* parallel to *AK*, and draw line *DA* to obtain the dimetric 90° angle *DAC*.

5.   Draw the large 15° ellipse on the box, and draw *XY* through the points on the ellipse where lines *AB* and *AC* cross the ellipse.

6.   From point *B*, draw *BC* parallel to *XY* to locate the proper length of *AC*.

7.   Draw the triangle *AED*, and measure the 15° angle which is the proper angle-size ellipse for the box lid.

8.   Draw the 15° ellipse on the box lid with the minor axis parallel to *DA* on the 15° ellipse.

PROBLEM SOLUTION

A 15°–15° dimetric exploded problem in which the ellipse is used for measuring is shown in Fig. 11-24.   This figure shows the solution for the angles, the angle-size ellipse on the inclined plane, and the nondimetric measurements of the pin and bushing along axis *XY*.   The problem is the same as is

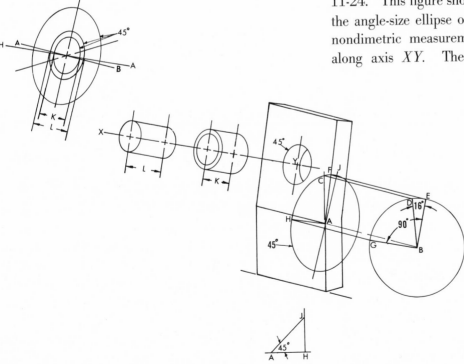

Fig. 11-24   Dimetric solution of angles, angle-size ellipse, and length of lines.

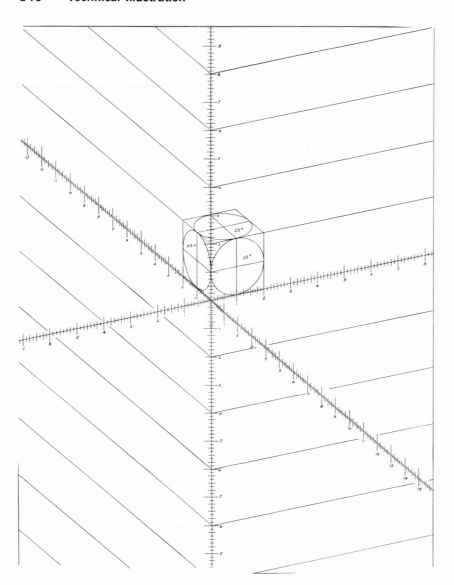

Fig. 11-25 Dimetric grid.

shown in Chap. 7, except that this is a dimetric drawing instead of isometric. Locate the points following in alphabetical order. The two small concentric 45° ellipses have a diameter equal to the desired length of the pin and bushing, and the proper nondimetric distance is obtained along axis *AH* which is parallel to *XY*. *AB* is the minor axis line for the concentric ellipse.

DIMETRIC AND TRIMETRIC GRIDS

Grids have been devised by industry for dimetric and trimetric illustration (Figs. 11-25 and 11-26), and occasionally they are used. The grids are made for a specific axis, and the proper foreshortened scales are shown along the axes. These grids show the

correct angle-size ellipse to use on the horizontal and vertical planes.

ELLIPSE WHEEL

The Lietz Ellipse Wheel, shown in Fig. 11-26, is a useful calculating device which rapidly and automatically determines the precise angle ellipse needed for a given horizontal or vertical plane in perspective, dimetric, or trimetric drawings. Select the desired axis, as at *D* for the left axis, which in this case is 40°, and at *E* for the right axis, or 15° in this case. The proper angle ellipse for the left vertical plane is shown at *A*, or 25°. The proper angle ellipse for the right vertical plane is shown at *C*, or 50°; and the proper angle ellipse for the horizontal plane is

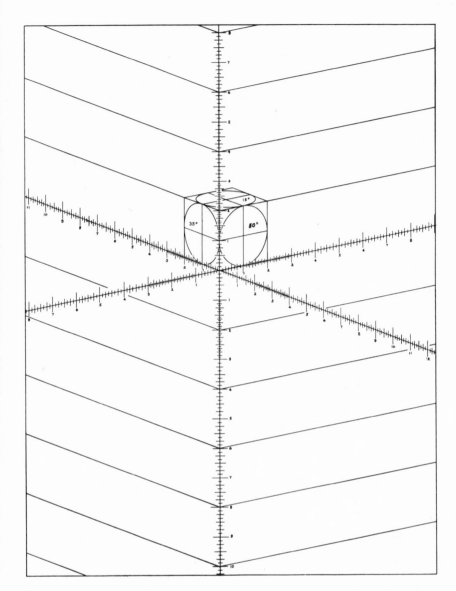

Fig. 11-26 Trimetric grid.

shown at B, or 30°. The plastic wheel will calculate 118 different drawing views if it is simply turned so that the arrows point to the desired axes. The proper size ellipse will appear in the three openings at A, B, and C.

Questions

1. What is the main difference between a dimetric drawing and an isometric drawing?
2. Define a dimetric drawing.
3. Define a trimetric drawing.
4. Give two different dimetric axes that represent horizontal surfaces.
5. What is an advantage of a dimetric drawing? Trimetric?
6. What is a disadvantage of a dimetric drawing? Trimetric?

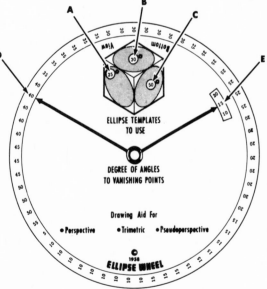

Fig. 11-27 Ellipse wheel. (The Lietz Co.)

7. What is shown on a dimetric grid?

8. Is the foreshortened scale the same for all dimetric drawings?   Explain.

Exercises

Dimetric and trimetric illustrations can be made from problems from Groups 1 through 10.

The primary difference between the isometric techniques shown previous to this chapter and the dimetric or trimetric methods is the use of the angle-size ellipse instead of the isometric ellipse.   The axes are different, and the scales are foreshortened, of course, but the different ellipse is the major exception.

Begin by drawing basic problems from Group 1, using different axes and revolving the 15°–15° and 10°–40° axes.   Use the revolved axes to obtain the desired view.

Select problems from Group 5 to practice the use of the ellipse as a measuring device.

Refer to Chaps. 5, 8, and 9, and draw problems from these chapters in dimetric and trimetric, utilizing the techniques explained.

Make a dimetric protractor using the circle-projection method explained in Chap. 7, and prepare foreshortened scales for different axes.   Use a large-diameter ellipse, at least 4″, to make protractors, because precise accuracy cannot be obtained otherwise.

Solve problems involving ellipses on nondimetric and nontrimetric planes.   Use the circle-projection technique.

12 SHADING TECHNIQUES AND PHOTO RETOUCHING

A minimum amount of shading is used in line technical illustration. Many illustrations are made without using line or surface shading. Most of the shading for line illustrations is limited to a type of line contrast shading or line delineation rather than surface shading, which is used extensively in commercial artwork with brochures, advertising, and proposals. Limited line shading is used particularly in engineering illustrations. A simple type of surface shading is occasionally used in publication illustrations.

LINE CONTRAST SHADING

When applying line contrast shading on illustrations the direction of the light source is first established. Normally, this is understood to be from the upper left at 45°, as shown on Fig. 12-1.

Generally three different weights of lines are used. The exterior lines are heavier and darker than the lines within an object. The three weights of lines are illustrated in Figs. 12-1 and 12-2. The lower and right side lines are three weight. The other outer-portion lines are two weight and the inner lines are one weight.

A chisel point on a pencil is desirable for the heavier pencil line shading and the various size pens for ink shading.

Lines showing the inner edges of an object often fade out, as shown in Figs. 12-2, 12-7, and 12-9. This is accomplished by slowly lifting the pencil or pen from the paper when drawing the line.

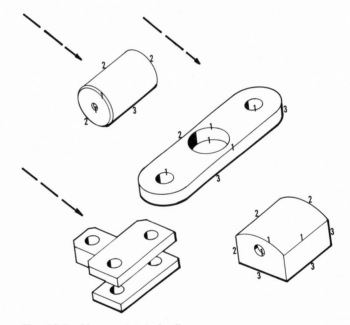

Fig. 12-1   Line contrast shading.

The lines showing the lower edge of cylindrical shafts, bolts, and hydraulic lines are made several times wider than the other lines, as illustrated in Figs. 12-1, 12-2, and 12-6.

Special Shading.   In most cases, surface shading is limited to the commercial artwork such as brochures, advertising, training aids, and proposals.

One of the more common types of surface shading is smudge shading, as indicated in Fig. 12-3. This is usually applied by pencil, although ink is also used. For best results using the pencil, take a piece

149

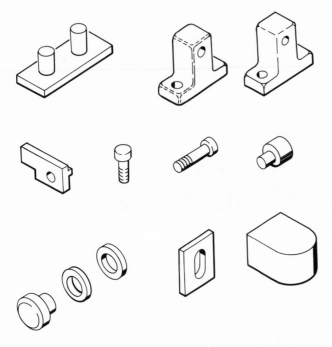

Fig. 12-2   Line contrast shading.

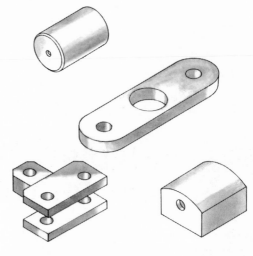

Fig. 12-3   Smudge shading.

of chamois skin and apply pencil dust from your pencil sharpener to the surface to be shaded.   The entire surface of an object may be covered, or highlights may be shown, as in Fig. 12-3.

Commercial products such as Artist-Aid, Zip-a-Tone, or Ben Day are used on some illustrations.   These products are cellophane sheets covered with spots, squares, parallel lines, or random shapes.   They may have an adhesive on one side that sticks to the illustration, or they may be a pressure-sensitive, rub-on material which is applied by merely being rubbed over the sheet.   (See Figs. 12-4 and 12-5.)   The pattern may be varied to simulate highlights, as in smudge shading.   Many patterns are available in this type of shading material.

Shading Holes.   The method used for shading holes is shown in Figs. 12-1 to 12-4, 12-6, and 12-7.   The shadow is placed on the side toward the light source, and it covers about one-third or less of the hole opening.   In shading, the amount will vary with different companies and in different situations.   The shade lines are drawn parallel to the hole.

Separate Planes.   In order to show separate planes in illustrations, lines which cross but in reality do not touch are broken, and a space equal to the thickness of the line is shown, as in Fig. 12-8.   Some

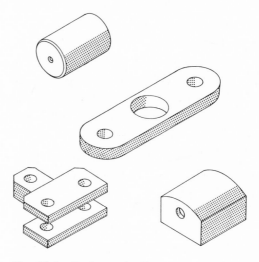

Fig. 12-4   Paste-up shading.

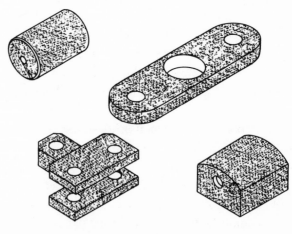

Fig. 12-5   Paste-up shading.

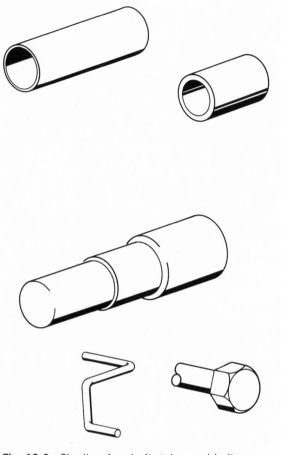

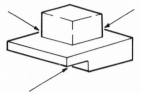

Fig. 12-8 Break in lines.

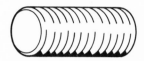

Fig. 12-9 Shading threads.

Fig. 12-6 Shading for shaft, tube, and bolt.

industries, however, do not use this technique. A break in the object lines is often shown when a center line or flow line crosses an object line. (See Chap. 9.)

Thread Shading. Shading of threads is shown in Figs. 12-2 and 12-9. The lower side of the bolt threads are shaded with an inverted V shape to accentuate the threads; however, many use a simplified method with only a heavy line. Highlights may be shown as illustrated.

Other Line-shading Techniques. Small thin washers, gaskets, rings, or small springs are completely shaded as drawn in Fig. 12-10.

Phantom lines are often used when parts of secondary importance must be drawn to show the location and position of a detailed part or assembly. (See Fig. 12-11.) The phantom line is a light line consisting of one long solid line and two short dashes. It is similar to the conventional cutting-plane line but much lighter.

Figure 12-12 shows a simplified method for shading

Fig. 12-10 Shading washers, springs, and O rings.

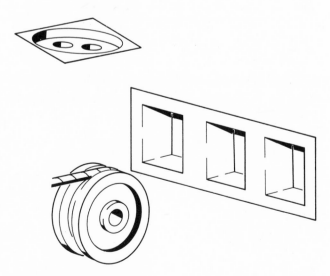

Fig. 12-7 Shading holes.

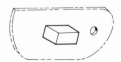

Fig. 12-11 Phantom lines.

Fig. 12-12   Shading wire bundle and cable.

small cables and wire bundles.   The curved lines are drawn freehand and show the outer shape of the cable or cable covering.   Shading for bolts and nuts is shown in Fig. 12-13.

ROSS-BOARD SHADING

Ross-board shading is shown in Fig. 12-14.   This is a white-surface board with varied embossed surfaces.   The shading is applied with pencil, crayon, brush, or ink, and the resulting appearance is unusual due to the grain of the board.

Fig. 12-13   Shading bolts and nuts.

Fig. 12-14   Ross-board shading.

Fig. 12-15   Scratchboard shading.

SCRATCHBOARD SHADING

This type of shading (Fig. 12-15) gives the appearance of an engraving.   The scratchboard has a smooth white surface that is painted with black ink.   The illustration is transferred to the black surface by carefully cutting with a needle or knife blade through the black inked surface to the white board.   This results in a white illustration on a black surface.

LINE HIGHLIGHT SHADING

An example of applying highlights to an illustration is shown in Fig. 12-16.   A random pattern of parallel lines is drawn to suggest light and dark areas.

SPECIAL SURFACE SHADING

A special type of surface shading is shown in Fig. 12-17.   This type of shading is seldom used on industrial line illustrations but is used in commercial artwork for brochures and advertising art.

This type of shading may be accomplished through a smudge process, prepared commercial patterns, airbrush, brush with inks, or line pattern.   It emphasizes highlights, shadows, and reflections from glass surfaces.   Random patterns are used and are mainly dependent upon the light source and reflections of light from the object.

PHOTO RETOUCHING

Photo retouching, as mentioned previously, may be a part of the work of a technical illustrator.   Since all photographs cannot be taken with ideal lighting and background, retouching must be done to ensure a clear picture.   This is done in several ways.   An airbrush or handbrush is used on the actual photo-

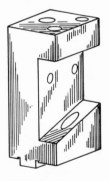

Fig. 12-16   Line surface shading.

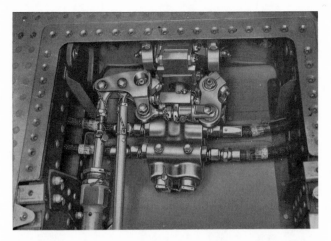

Fig. 12-19 Photo after retouching. (North American Aviation, Inc.)

graph to add light or dark shades, lines are sometimes scratched on the negative, or undesirable detail is blotted out with a special dark lacquer.

An original photograph is shown in Fig. 12-18, and the same photograph is shown in Fig. 12-19 after retouching.

Questions

1. What type of shading is used in most technical illustrations?
2. What commercial products are sometimes used for shading?
3. How are exterior lines of an object shaded?
4. What part of a shaft or bolt is shaded?
5. How are holes shaded?
6. What type of pencil point is suggested for shading?
7. What is meant by smudge shading?
8. What is photo retouching, and how is it accomplished?
9. Describe a special method sometimes used in pencil shading.
10. What method of line delineation is used when one line of an object extends behind another line?

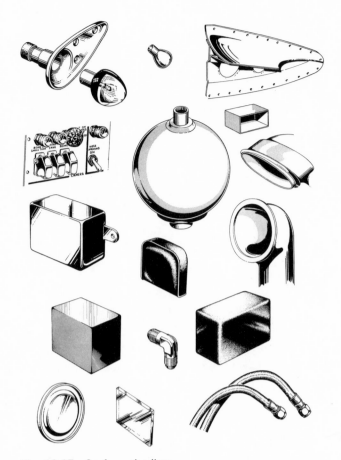

Fig. 12-17 Surface shading.

Fig. 12-18 Photo before retouching. (North American Aviation, Inc.)

13 OBLIQUE DRAWING

Oblique drawing is seldom used in technical illustration in industry; however, it is discussed here in order to complete the presentation of the traditional three-dimensional methods of illustration.

An oblique drawing is a three-dimensional drawing with one surface parallel to the plane of projection, or the plane of the paper, and the other surfaces drawn along a receding axis that forms an angle with the horizontal. This angle is usually 30, 45, or 60° (Figs. 13-1 to 13-3) for convenience, although any angle may be used except 90°. True dimensions are measured along the three axes except in special cases described later.

Oblique drawing is the simplest method of making a three-dimensional drawing. Because of excessive distortion, however, this system is seldom used for a finished drawing. Because of its simplicity, oblique drawing may be used satisfactorily for rough freehand sketching. It is also an easy way of making the transition from orthographic drawings to three-dimensional drawings (see Fig. 13-4).

Several variations are used in general oblique drawing, as shown by Figs. 13-2 and 13-3 where the axis is reversed and revolved.

REVERSED-AXIS OBLIQUE

Reversed-axis oblique is used to show the bottom view of an object as illustrated in Fig. 13-2. Instead

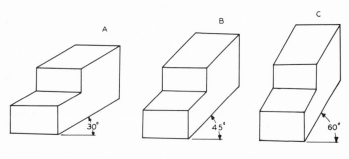

Fig. 13-1 Regular oblique.

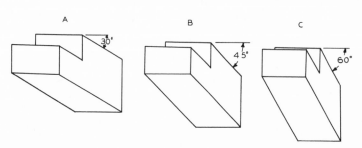

Fig. 13-2 Reversed-axis oblique.

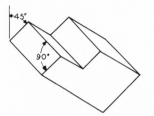

Fig. 13-3 Revolved-axis oblique.

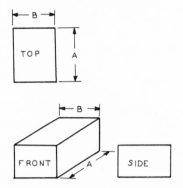

Fig. 13-4 Drawing oblique from three views.

of being drawn above and upward from the horizontal, the receding axis is drawn downward and below the horizontal.

REVOLVED-AXIS OBLIQUE

Revolved-axis oblique is used when details can be shown in a more desirable way, as illustrated in Fig. 13-3. In revolved-axis oblique, the vertical axis is tilted at an angle, but the angle between the axis on the front surface remains at true 90°, while the receding axis may vary as before.

FORESHORTENED SCALE

Some illustrators use a special foreshortened system of measurement along the receding axis for general oblique. The vertical dimensions and the horizontal dimensions along the axis which is parallel to the picture plane are made true. The greater the angle of the receding axis, the less the foreshortening, because the distortion appears less when the angle is greater. For example, if the receding axis is 30°, the foreshortening used may be one-half of the actual dimensions. If the receding axis is 45°, the foreshortening would be less, or about three-fourths of the actual dimensions (see Figs. 13-5 and 13-6). This special foreshortening is used to reduce distortion.

DESIRED POSITION OF OBJECT

When making an oblique drawing, it is better to place the main characteristics of an object along the surface that is parallel to the picture plane, as in Fig. 13-7. The shape of an object is true shape when drawn on the plane that is parallel to the picture plane. On this plane irregular surfaces can be easily drawn in true shape, and they will have a more pleasing appearance to the eye.

The longest dimension of an object will make a better appearance if placed along the horizontal axis, since there is less distortion (see Fig. 13-8). Sometimes a choice must be made whether to place the longest dimension along the horizontal axis or the part of the object with the main characteristics along this

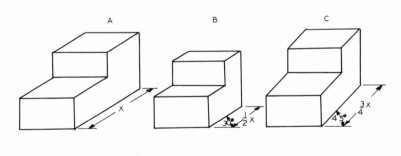

Fig. 13-5 Oblique foreshortened.

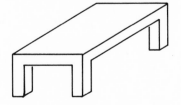

Fig. 13-6 Cabinet drawing.

Fig. 13-7 Oblique of irregular object.

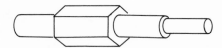

Fig. 13-8 Oblique in recommended position.

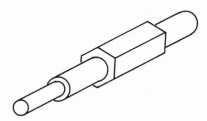

Fig. 13-9 Oblique not recommended.

axis (Fig. 13-9). Generally speaking, it is better to place the longest dimension along this axis regardless of the main characteristics. This is especially true if there is considerable difference between the length and width of the object as in Fig. 13-8. The circles and hexagons cannot be drawn in true shape in Fig. 13-8, but with templates available they are just as easy to draw as if they were in true shape.

CAVALIER DRAWING

In addition to general oblique drawing, there are two special methods for making oblique drawings: *cavalier drawing* and *cabinet drawing*.

When an oblique drawing is made with the receding axis at 45°, it is called cavalier (see Fig. 13-1). All dimensions are drawn true on the axis of this drawing.

CABINET DRAWING

When the oblique drawing is made with the dimensions foreshortened one-half on the receding axis, it is called cabinet drawing (see Fig. 13-6). The angle of the receding axis may vary. The effect of foreshortening is shown in Fig. 13-6. True dimensions are used in one view and one-half true in the other.

When drawing an ellipse and hexagon bolts and nuts on oblique drawings, take care to avoid distortion. Refer to Chap. 4 for the proper industrial methods.

Questions

1. What is an advantage of oblique drawing? A disadvantage?
2. What is an oblique drawing called when made with a receding axis at 45°?
3. Define a cabinet drawing.
4. What is the purpose of foreshortening dimensions on an oblique drawing?
5. Make an oblique view of a hexagon-head bolt in a vertical position.
6. What oblique method should be used when drawing a long shaft?
7. When does distortion appear the greatest in oblique drawing?
8. On what plane of an oblique drawing are details of an object drawn in true shape?

Exercise

Extreme distortion is prevalent in oblique drawings especially when round holes, arcs, and cylindrical shapes are involved. Because of this, select problems with these shapes only on the frontal plane where these shapes appear in their true shapes; otherwise, the use of the ellipse template makes it difficult to avoid distortion.

Draw several problems from Group 1, Chap. 3, using the cabinet method and the regular oblique. Limit the amount of time spent drawing oblique, because less than one-tenth of 1 per cent of technical illustrations are made in oblique.

14 INKING METHODS AND EQUIPMENT

Modern drafting materials and improved reproduction equipment have reduced the amount of inking required in technical illustration; however, there is still considerable work that must be done in ink. Most publications work must be inked. With the aid of modern equipment, inking has become less hazardous and time-consuming.

INKING PENS

Several inking pens are available for line work, and all of them do a satisfactory job.

THE WRICO PEN

Figure 14-1 shows the separate parts of the Wrico pen and the size of the points available. The various-size points can be easily changed for the width of line desired. This pen can be used for line work as well as for accurate lettering, using lettering guides. The Wrico Universal Scriber, shown in Fig. 14-2, is used with guides that have letters engraved on a strip of Vinylite. One point is placed in the grooves of the letters, and the other point, which holds the ink, forms the accurate letters.

LEROY LETTERING PEN

The Leroy lettering pen (Fig. 14-3) is a well-known device which is widely used for accurate lettering as well as line work. It can be obtained with various lettering guides with grooved letters. With this pen one point moves in the guide while another point, which is attached to a small mechanism and comes in various sizes, makes accurate letters. Leroy pen points can also be used with lettering guides consisting of plastic sheets with cutout letters. The points are

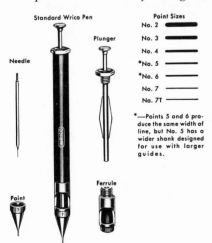

Fig. 14-1 Wrico pen. (Charles Bruning Co., Inc.)

Fig. 14-2 Wrico Scriber. (Charles Bruning Co., Inc.)

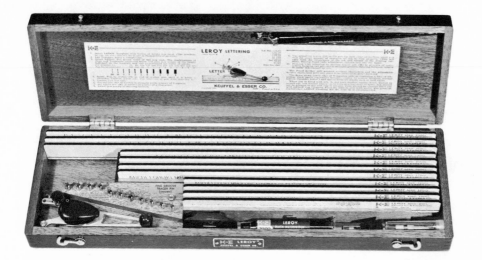

Fig. 14-3 Leroy lettering set. (Keuffel & Esser Co.)

attached to a special pen-point holder (Fig. 14-4), and in this way they are used for line work. Leroy pens with a plastic reservoir for ink are available and can be used with the lettering set or for line work.

THE RAPIDOGRAPH PEN

The Rapidograph pen (Fig. 14-5) by Koh-I-Noor Pencil Co., Inc. is a technical pen which may be obtained with various-size points. One type has the plastic ink reservoir, and the other type retains the ink in the barrel.

THE MARS TECHNICAL PEN

The Mars technical pen is another type of pen that is used for line work as well as lettering with guides. This pen can be purchased in various sizes and may retain the ink in the barrel or have the plastic ink reservoir. The pen is shown in Fig. 14-6.

Fig. 14-5 Rapidograph pen. (Kok-I-Noor Pencil Co., Inc.)

THE GRAPHOS PEN

The Graphos pen (Fig. 14-7) is a type of technical pen which has many points of different styles and sizes. This pen can be used for both line work and lettering.

All the pens described above can easily be used with templates as well as straight line work and lettering. Constant cleaning is unnecessary, and there is a continuous supply of ink.

Fig. 14-4 Leroy pen point with holder. (North American Aviation, Inc.)

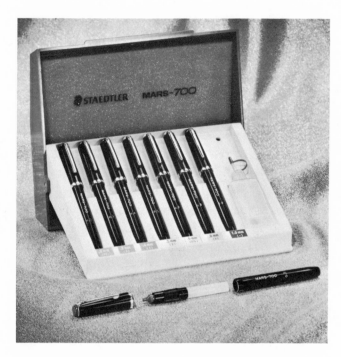

Fig. 14-6   Mars pens.   (J. S. Staedtler, Inc.)

Fig. 14-7   Graphos pen.   (Gunther Wagner.)

RULING PEN

The conventional ruling pen is used for straight line work but is difficult to use with ellipse and hexagon templates or lettering guides.

SPECIAL PEN POINTS

There are a number of special pen points available for freehand lettering in ink. Speedball pen points, shown in Fig. 14-8, can be purchased in various sizes and shapes and can be used for almost any desired letter. Four types of points are available: the *A*, or square; the *B*, or round; the *C*, or flat; and the *D*, or oval point. These points are used with an ordinary penholder and, because of the nature of the point, glide easily over the inking surface. Figure 14-9 shows a recommended method for using Speedball points.

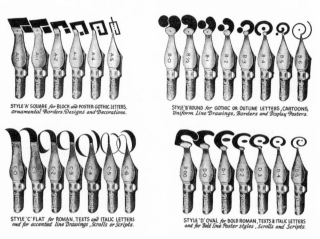

STYLE 'A' SQUARE *for* BLOCK *and* POSTER GOTHIC LETTERS, ornamental Borders Designs and Decorations.

STYLE 'B' ROUND *for* GOTHIC OR OUTLINE LETTERS, CARTOONS, Uniform Line Drawings, Borders and Display Posters.

STYLE 'C' FLAT *for* ROMAN, TEXTS *and* ITALIC LETTERS and *for* accented line Drawings, Scrolls or Scripts.

STYLE 'D' OVAL *for* BOLD ROMAN, TEXTS & ITALIC LETTERS and *for* Bold line Poster styles, Scrolls and Scripts.

Fig. 14-8   Speedball points.   (The Lietz Co.)

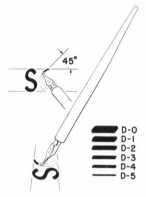

Fig. 14-9   Lettering with Speedball points.   (North American Aviation, Inc.)

Fig. 14-10   Brush pen.   (Wood Regan Co.)

Gillott pen points are popular for inking letters and dimensions and are available in various sizes and styles.

The Wrico brush pen, shown in Fig. 14-10, is used mainly for lettering with guides, although it may also be used for line work. This pen is frequently used for chart work where wide lines are needed.

There are numerous types of felt pens which are used mainly in technical illustration for chart work. They are usually disposable, although some types can be refilled. They can be purchased with ink of different colors. Many of these pens have a nylon tip instead of a felt one.

INKING PROCEDURES

Most drawings are inked by placing a sheet of vellum, drafting film (Mylar), or tracing cloth (linen) over the pencil drawing and inking over the pencil lines which show through. In this way, if the ink is smeared, the pencil drawing will not be ruined. Pencil drawings made on vellum, tracing cloth, and illustration board are also inked directly over graphite, blue, or purple pencil lines.

Drawings are inked on Strathmore paper. The pencil drawing is made on the Strathmore paper, and the inked lines are then placed directly over the pencil lines. Another method is the use of a sheet of carbon paper between the pencil drawing and the Strathmore paper. In this way the carbon lines are made lightly on the Strathmore and are then inked.

A fine powder such as Pounce may be rubbed in lightly on the surface and then removed with a brush, when the inking is being done on vellum, cloth, or drafting film. Chalk dust from a blackboard eraser may be used if no commercial powder is available.

STEPS IN INKING

Many of the pitfalls of inking may be avoided if the illustrator follows an orderly procedure for inking a problem. Circles, arcs, and irregular curves should be inked first, beginning at the top of the drawing and moving downward. It is much easier to make a straight line tangent to an arc than it is to make an arc tangent to two straight lines. Care should be taken to allow sufficient time for lines to dry before moving triangles, ellipses, the T square, or the drafting machine over the drawing. Straight lines are then inked, starting again from the top of the drawing and moving downward.

The illustrator must be careful to keep ink from running beneath templates, triangles, the arm of the drafting machine, or the T square to avoid blots and smears. Several methods are used to avoid this common pitfall of inking. One simple method is to place one triangle over another or one ellipse over another to raise the edge off the paper. In this way the triangle or ellipse template will not come in contact with the inked line. Some equipment is available with beveled edges for the purpose of avoiding ink smears. Another common method for holding

the equipment above the paper is to paste thin pieces of cork or several thicknesses of drafting tape on the surface of the equipment.

Ink lines can be erased in various ways. Some prefer to do this entirely with an eraser or by scratching with a knife or razor blade. For drafting film some use a liquid such as ammonia or benzine or prepared commercial products. Care must be taken, regardless of the method used, particularly if another line must be placed over the erased surface. If the surface is damaged, soapstone may be rubbed over vellum to fill the pores. A white lacquer is often used to cover the unwanted ink line.

Inking pens must be kept clean, and any of the commercial pen cleaners or a diluted solution of ammonia may be used. A good inker is one with a steady hand and a lot of patience.

Questions

1. Name three mechanical pens used for inking lines.
2. Give the names of two special letter devices.
3. Describe several methods used to avoid smearing lines when using mechanical aids.
4. Name four Speedball pen points.
5. What is the main use of Speedball pen points?
6. Name three materials on which inked drawings are made.
7. What is the suggested order of inking straight lines and arcs?
8. What are the main qualifications for a good inker?
9. What is used to clean inking pens?
10. Describe the procedure used for inking a pencil illustration.

Exercises

Select several problems from Group 1, details, and ink on a clean sheet of vellum placed over the pencil drawing. Also, ink problems from this group which have been drawn on vellum with blue or purple pencils. Place the ink lines directly over these lines. Ink several problems on drafting film by placing the film over the pencil drawing. Ink several problems on tracing cloth, Strathmore, and illustration board.

Ink one exploded-assembly drawing on vellum, tracing cloth, drafting film, and illustration board. Make use of white lacquer to paint over unwanted ink lines.

PROBLEMS: GROUP 10
Assemblies

The assemblies shown in this group will provide the necessary experience in planning layouts; exploding parts; showing the required flow lines, index numbers, and leaders; drawing spot details, possible enlargements, and revolved views. Do not attempt large assemblies until you have mastered the basic techniques of technical illustration by drawing single parts and small subassemblies.

Make an accurate freehand sketch of the assemblies first, in order to plan the proper layout, analyze the blueprint, and be sure all parts are shown. An accurate illustration is practically worthless without an accurate layout and placement of parts. Considerable time and thought is required to become a good technical illustrator.

Various types of shading can be applied; however, in the majority of line illustrations, only a simple line contrast method is used. Reserve the elaborate shading for brochures and advertising art. Some illustration groups do no shading on line illustrations.

Several of these assemblies have no dimensions. Use the dividers to obtain measurements since this is a common practice in technical illustration, even when dimensions are shown.

PROB. 10-1 Machinist's vise.

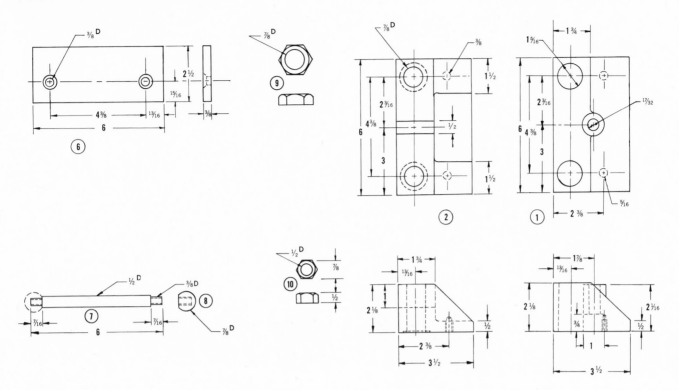

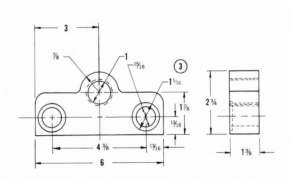

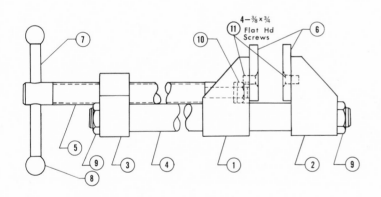

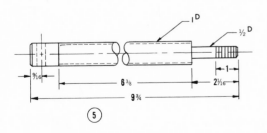

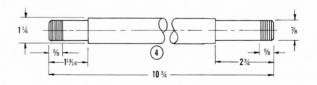

PROB. 10-2   Table-adjustment assembly.

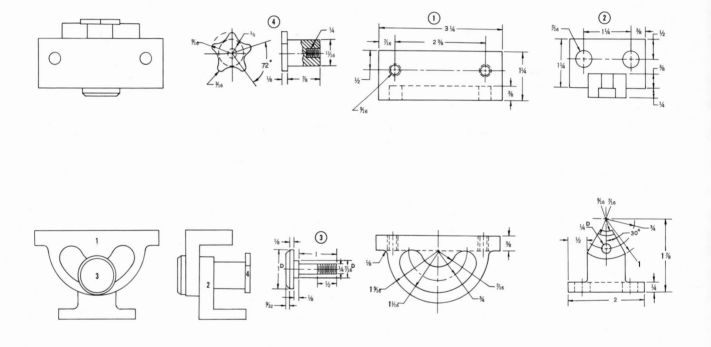

PROB. 10-3   Valve.

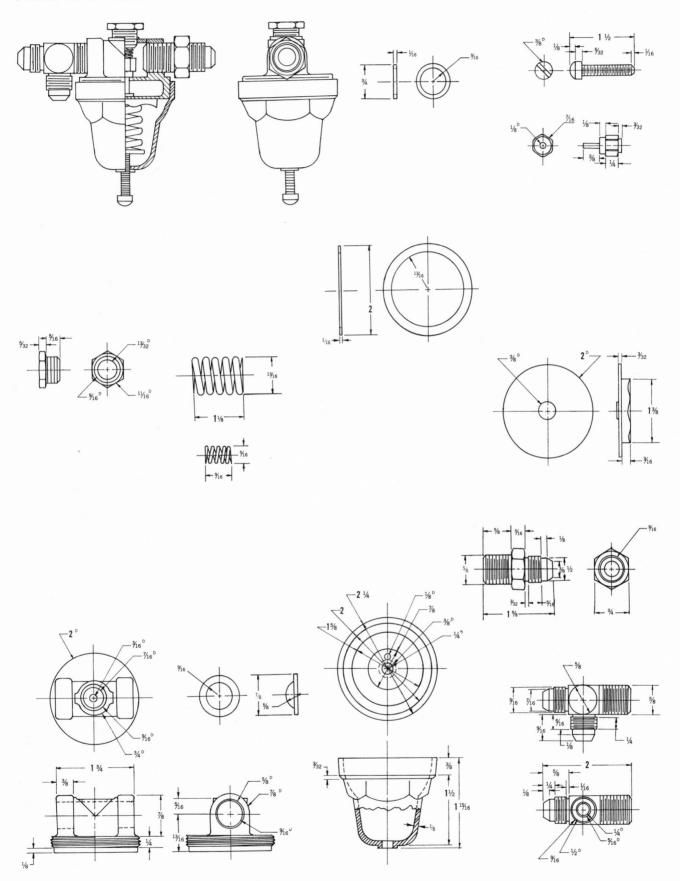

PROB. 10-4　Trailer hitch.

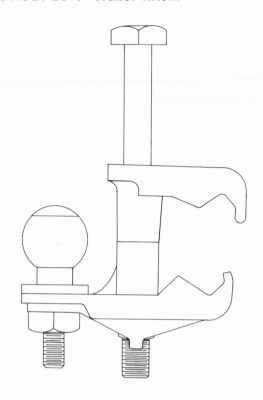

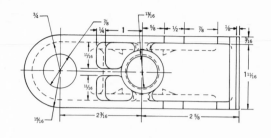

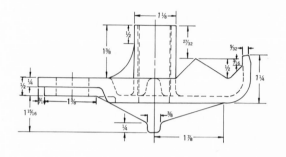

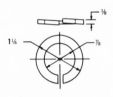

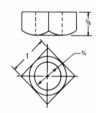

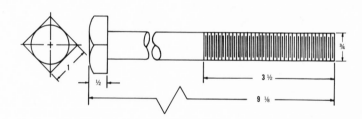

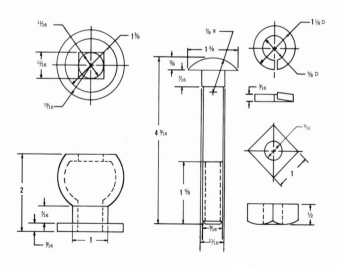

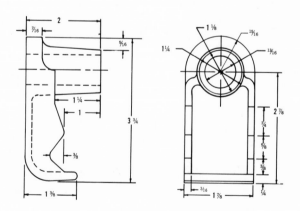

166

PROB. 10-5 Belt roller.

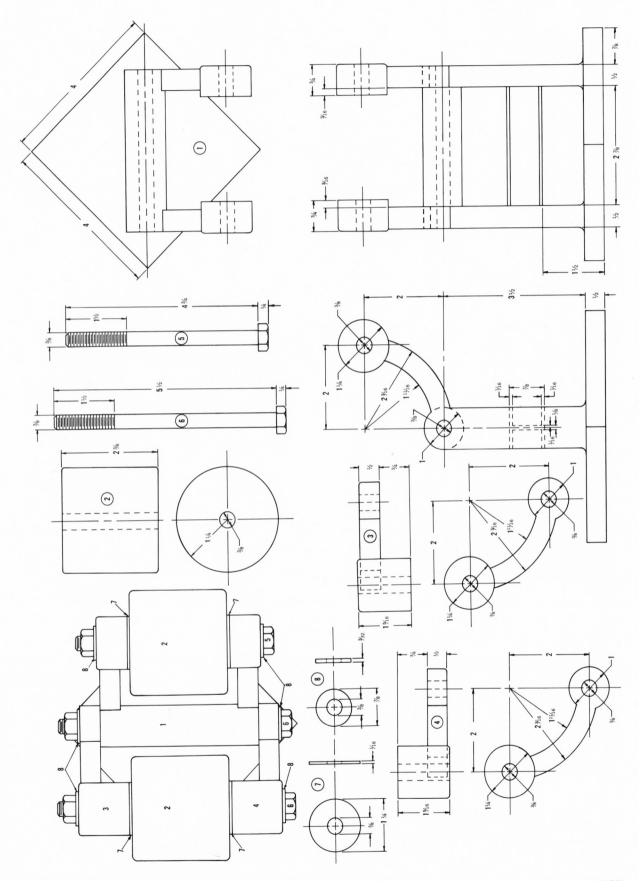

PROB. 10-6 Vise base.

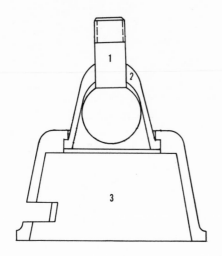

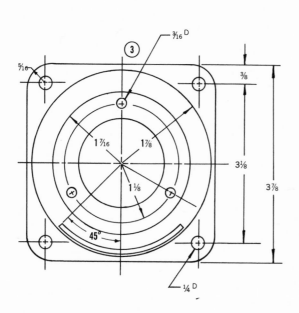

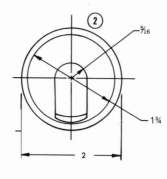

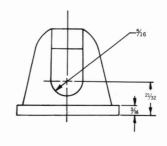

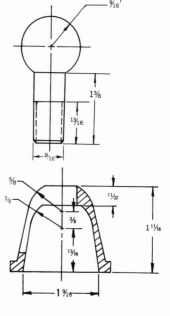

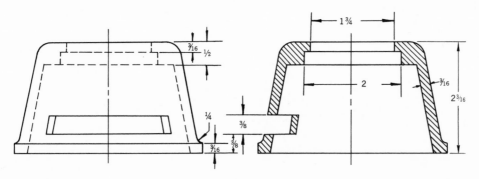

PROB. 10-7 Belt pulley.

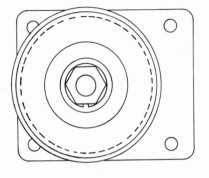

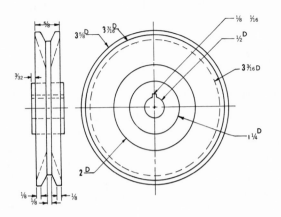

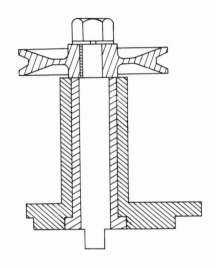

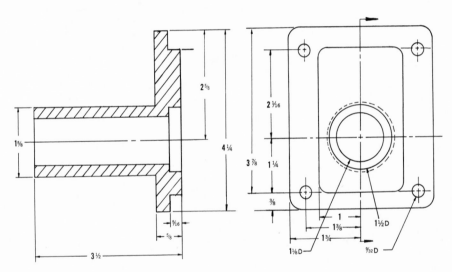

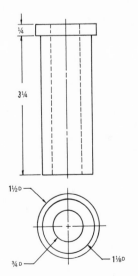

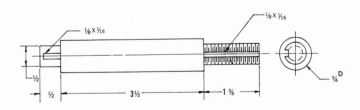

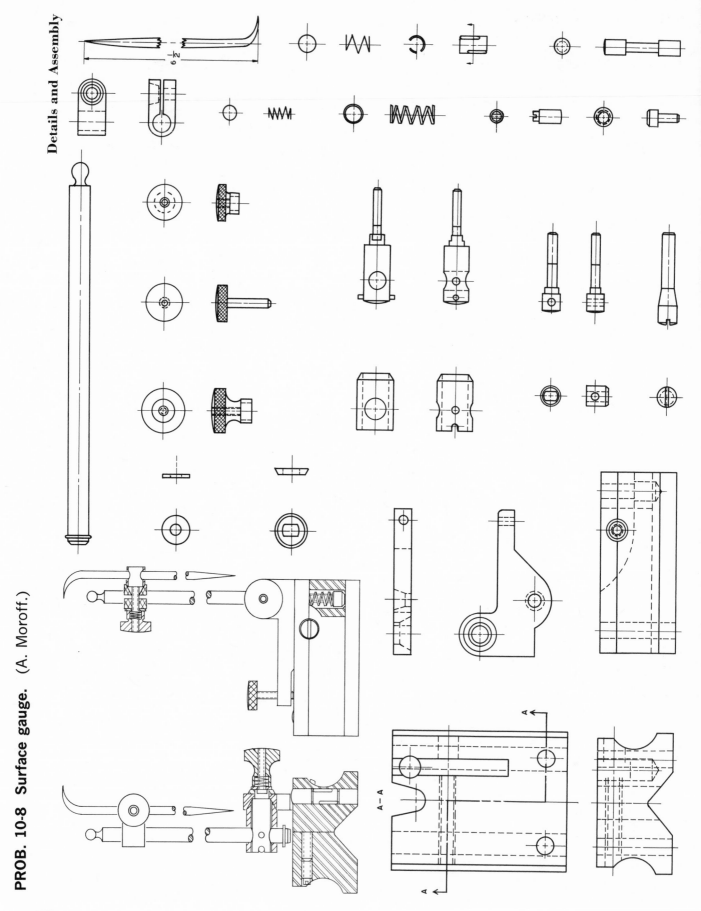

PROB. 10-8 Surface gauge. (A. Moroff.)

PROB. 10-9 Grinder rest brackets. (J. Bates.)

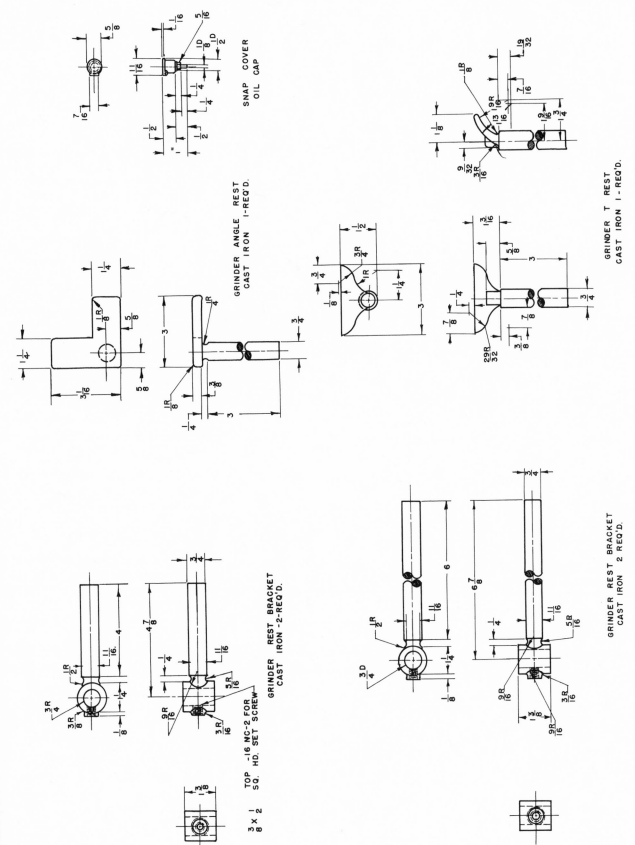

SNAP COVER
OIL CAP

GRINDER ANGLE REST
CAST IRON 1-REQ'D.

GRINDER T REST
CAST IRON 1 - REQ'D.

GRINDER REST BRACKET
CAST IRON -2-REQ'D.

GRINDER REST BRACKET
CAST IRON 2 REQ'D.

TOP -16 NC-2 FOR
SQ. HD. SET SCREW

$3 \times \frac{1}{8} \times 2$

PROB. 10-10 Bracket. (Boeing Airplane Co.)

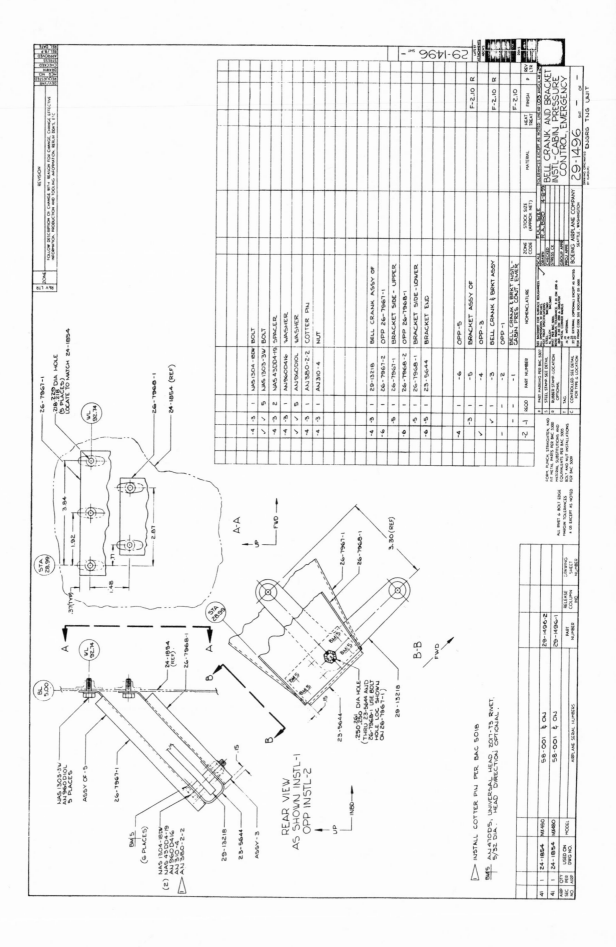

172

PROB. 10-11 General-location drawing: Boeing 707. (Boeing Airplane Co.)

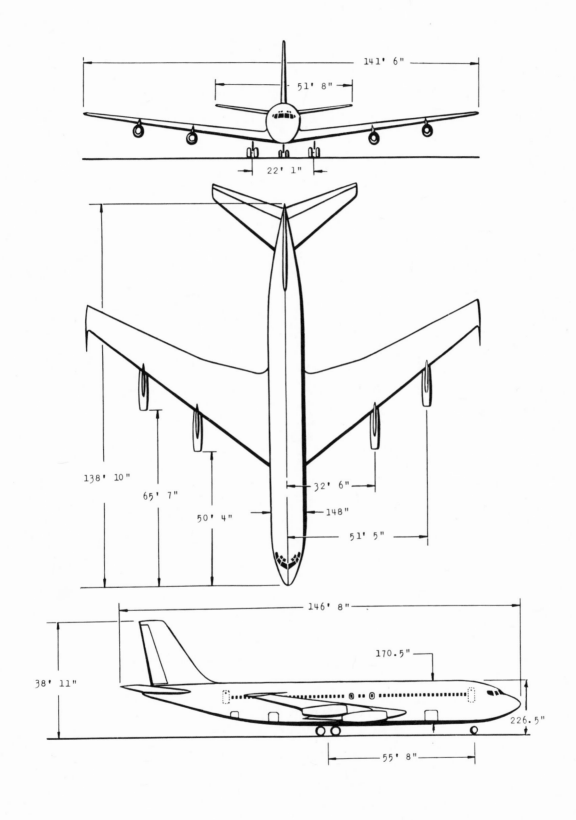

PROB. 10-12 Aircraft frame. (North American Aviation, Inc.)

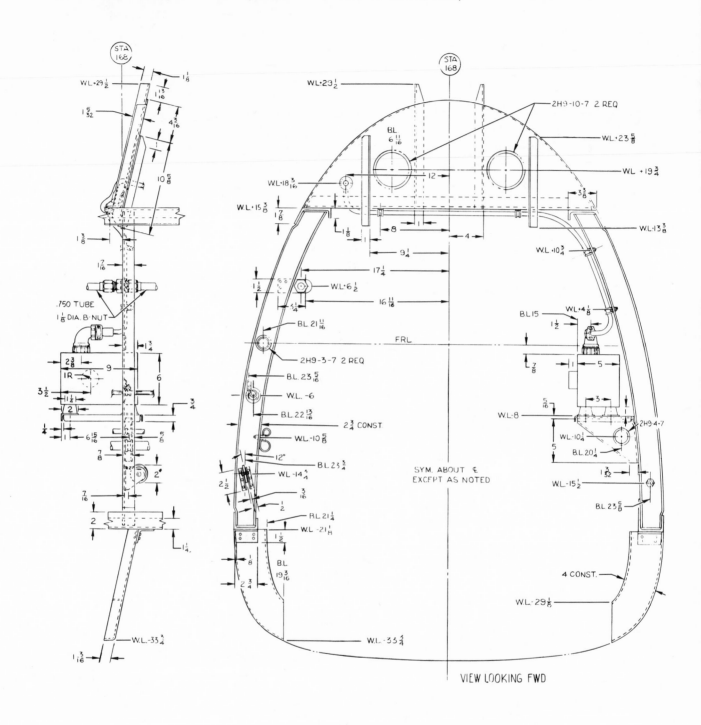

VIEW LOOKING FWD

SCALE

174

PROB. 10-13 Link assembly. (Douglas Aircraft Co., Inc.)

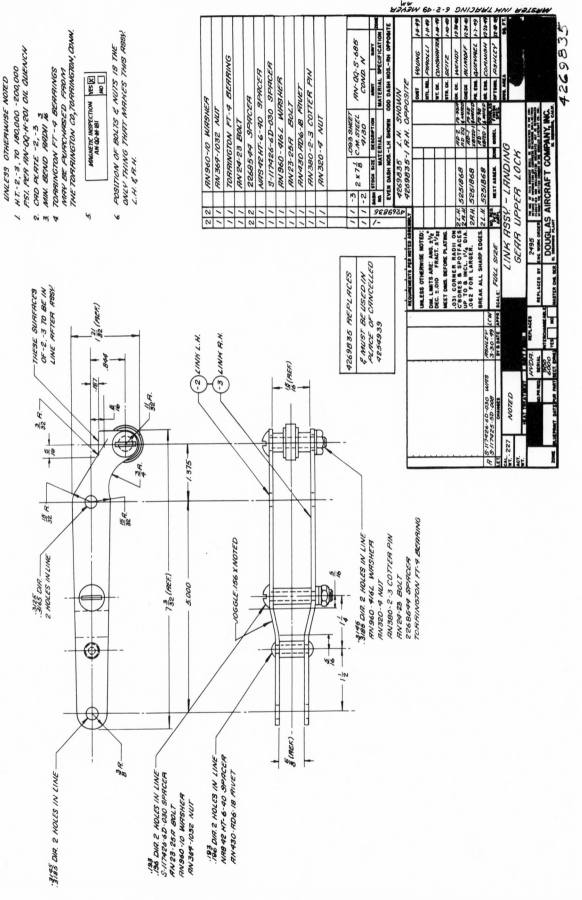

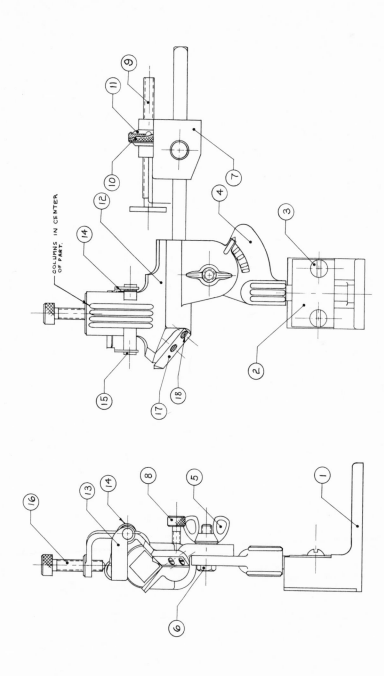

PROB. 10-14 Drill grinding attachment. (L. Stakelbeck.)

COLUMNS IN CENTER OF PART.

Drill grinding attachment

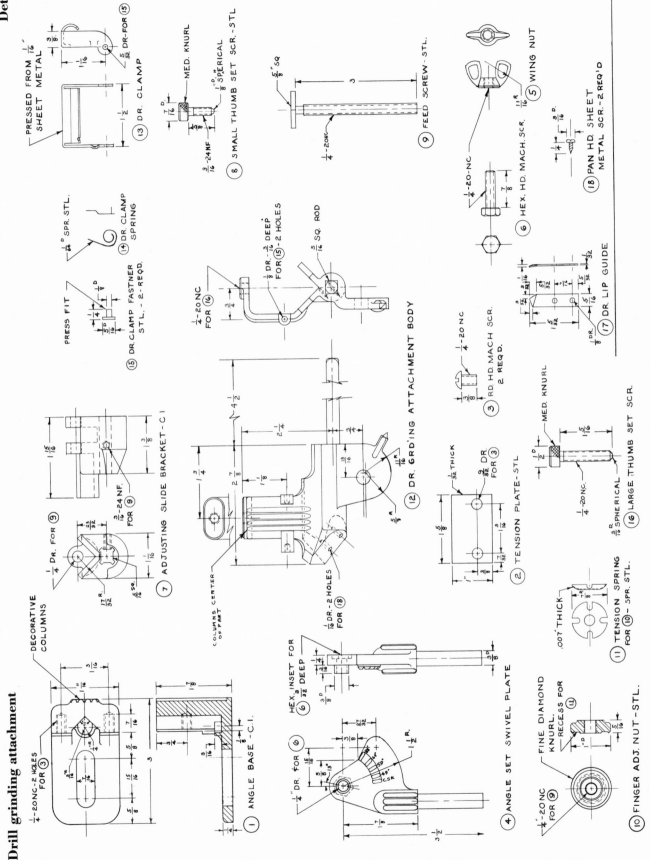

PROB. 10-15 Canopy-actuating mechanism. (North American Aviation, Inc.)

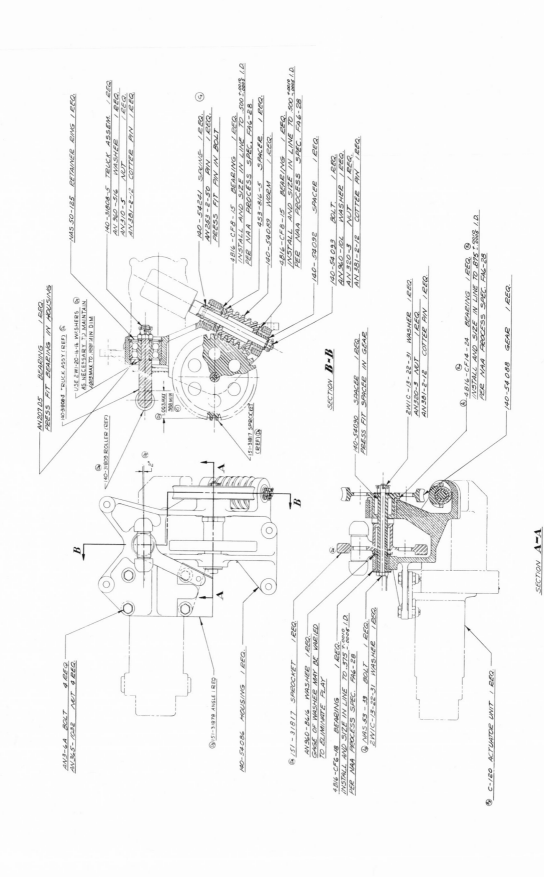

Canopy actuating mechanism

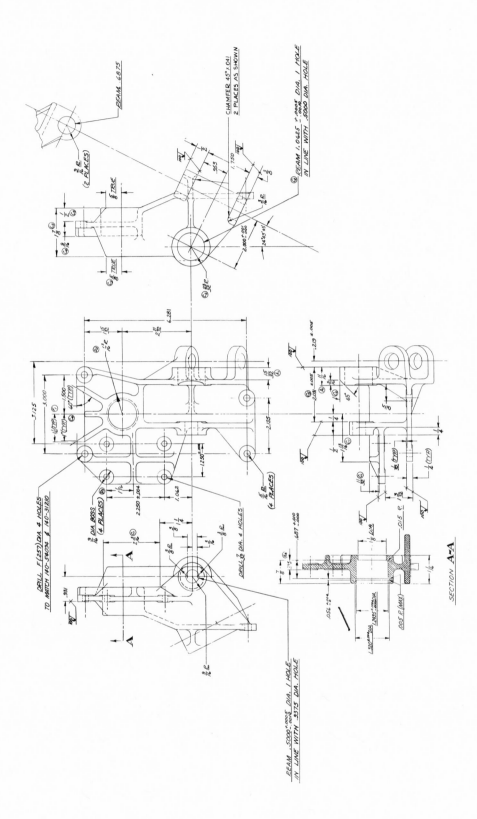

Canopy actuating mechanism

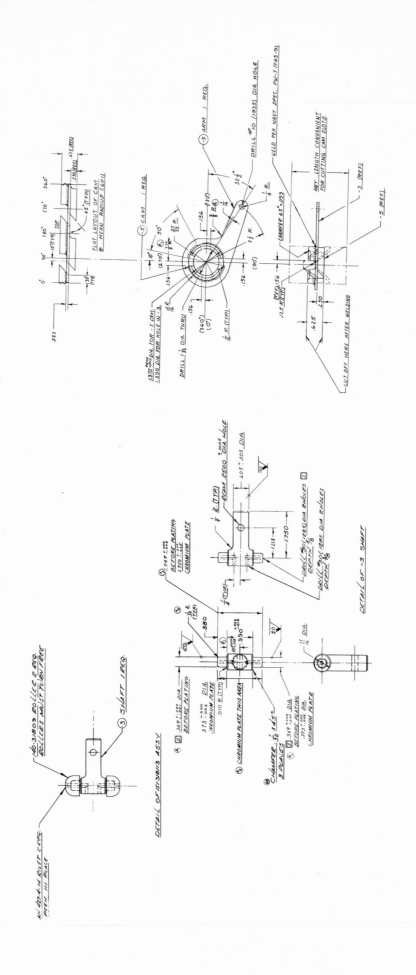

Canopy actuating mechanism

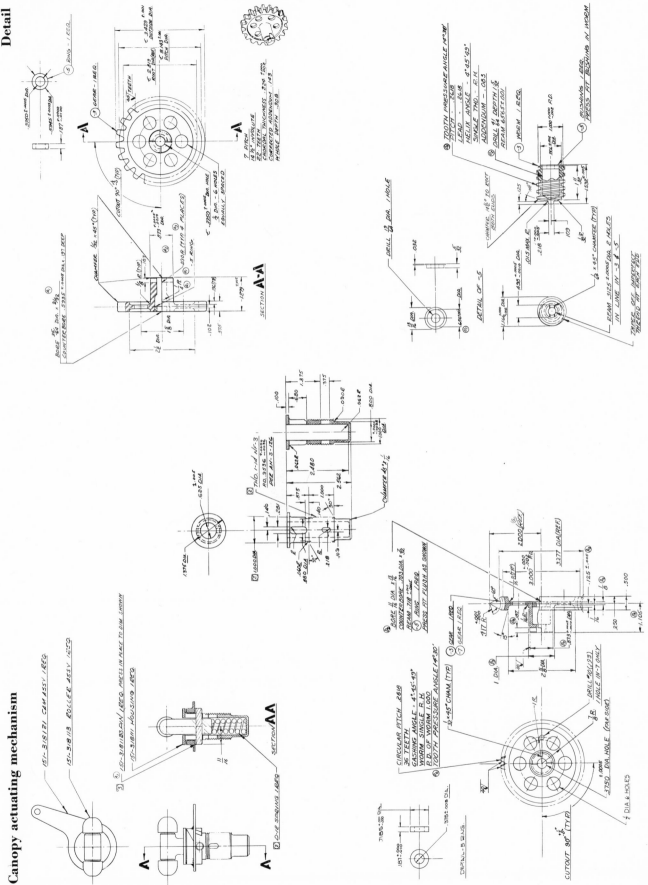

PROB. 10-16 Landing-gear drag brace. (North American Aviation, Inc.)

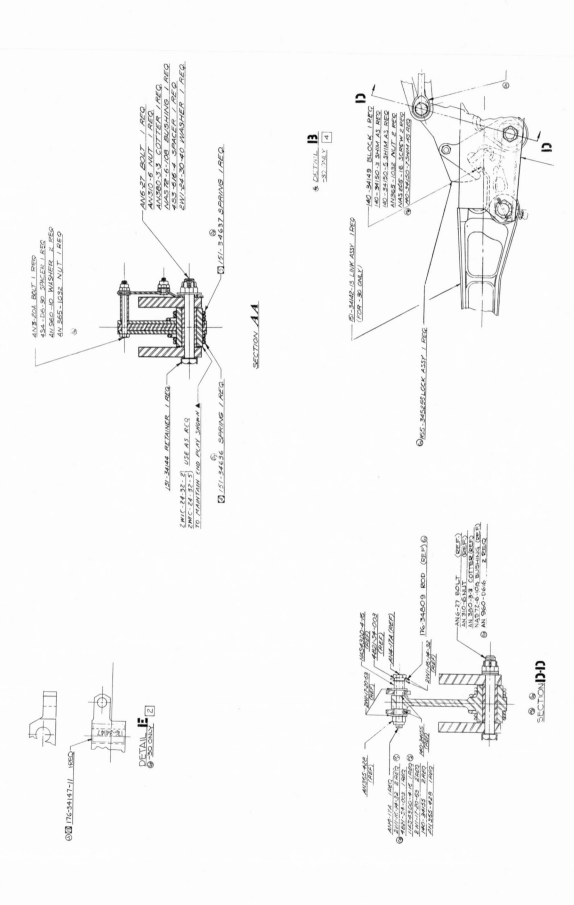

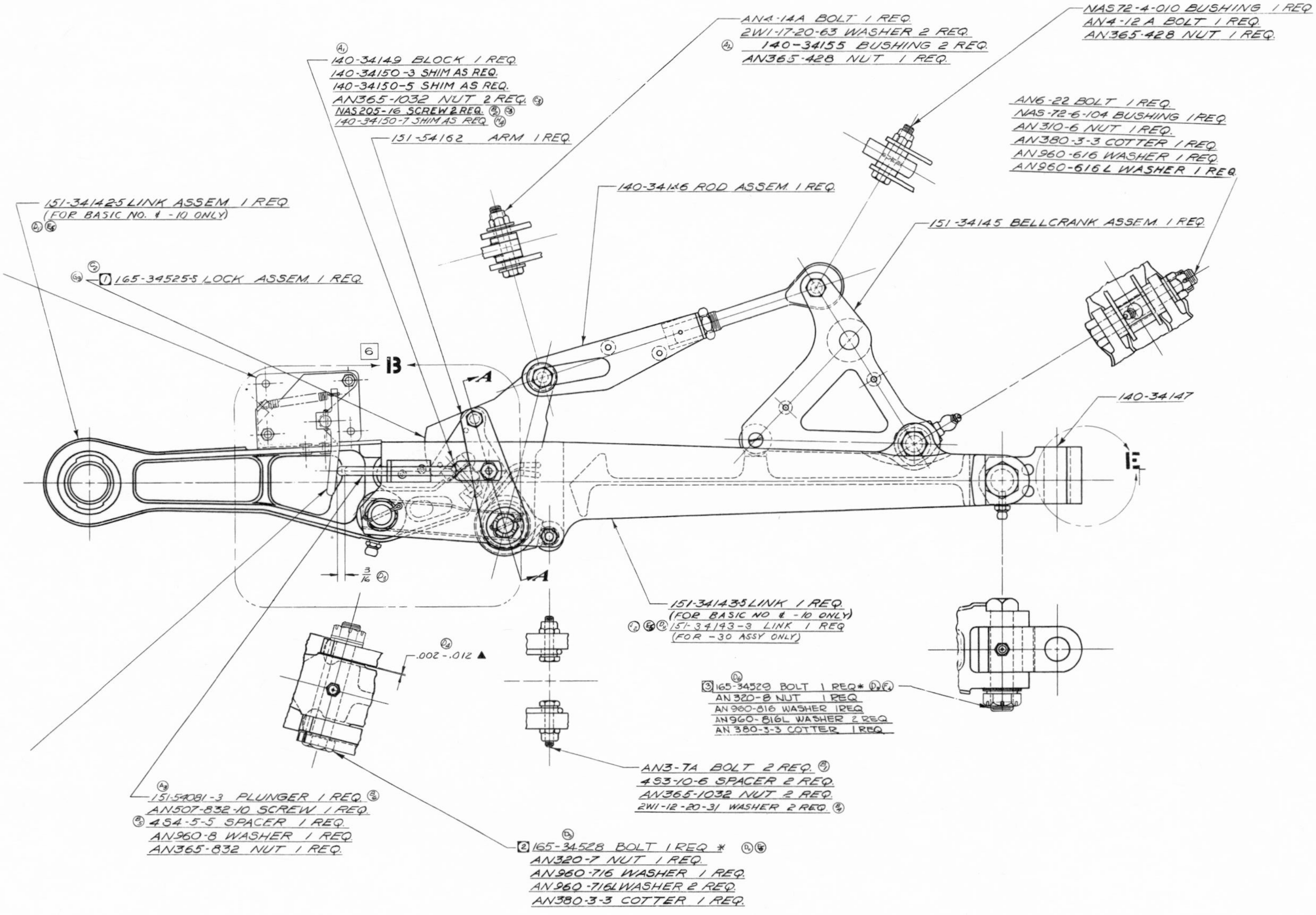

NAS72-4-010 BUSHING 1 REQ.
AN4-12A BOLT 1 REQ.
AN365-428 NUT 1 REQ.

AN6-22 BOLT 1 REQ.
NAS72-6/04 BUSHING 1 REQ.
AN310-6 NUT 1 REQ.
AN380-3-3 COTTER 1 REQ.
AN960-616 WASHER 1 REQ.
AN960-616 L WASHER 1 REQ.

151-34145 BELLCRANK ASSEM 1 REQ.

140-34147

AN4-14A BOLT 1 REQ.
2W1-17-20-63 WASHER 2 REQ.
140-34155 BUSHING 2 REQ.
AN365-428 NUT 1 REQ.

151-34143S LINK 1 REQ.
(FOR BASIC NO. 1-10 ONLY)
151-34143-3 LINK 1 REQ.
(FOR -30 ASSY ONLY)

165-34529 BOLT 1 REQ.*
AN320-8 NUT 1 REQ.
AN960-816 WASHER 1 REQ.
AN960-816L WASHER 2 REQ.
AN380-3-3 COTTER 1 REQ.

AN3-7A BOLT 2 REQ.
453-10-6 SPACER 2 REQ.
AN365-1032 NUT 2 REQ.
2W1-12-20-31 WASHER 2 REQ.

165-34528 BOLT 1 REQ.*
AN320-7 NUT 1 REQ.
AN960-716 WASHER 1 REQ.
AN960-716L WASHER 2 REQ.
AN380-3-3 COTTER 1 REQ.

140-34149 BLOCK 1 REQ.
140-34150-3 SHIM AS REQ.
140-34150-5 SHIM AS REQ.
AN365-1032 NUT 2 REQ.
NAS205-16 SCREW 2 REQ.
140-34150-7 SHIM AS REQ.

151-54162 ARM 1 REQ.

140-34146 ROD ASSEM 1 REQ.

151-34142S LINK ASSEM 1 REQ.
(FOR BASIC NO. 1-10 ONLY)

165-345255 LOCK ASSEM 1 REQ.

151-54081-3 PLUNGER 1 REQ.
AN507-832-10 SCREW 1 REQ.
454-5-5 SPACER 1 REQ.
AN960-8 WASHER 1 REQ.
AN365-832 NUT 1 REQ.

.200-.012

$\frac{3}{16}$

Landing-gear drag brace

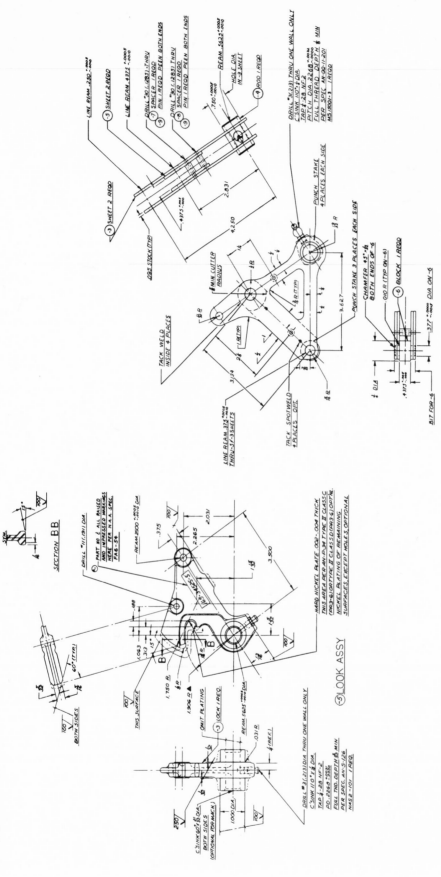

Landing-gear drag brace

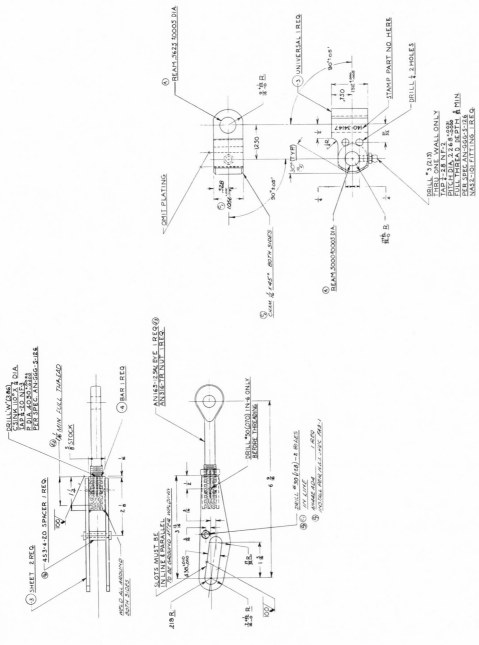

Landing-gear drag brace

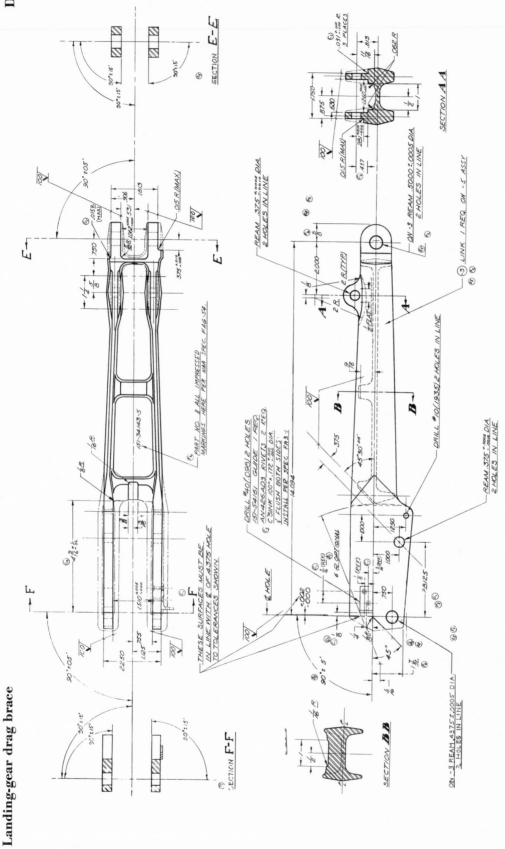

Landing-gear drag brace

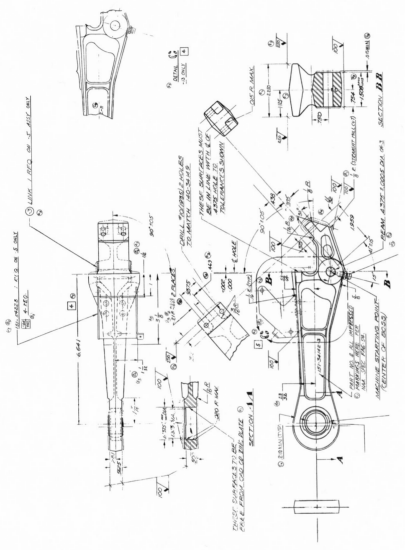

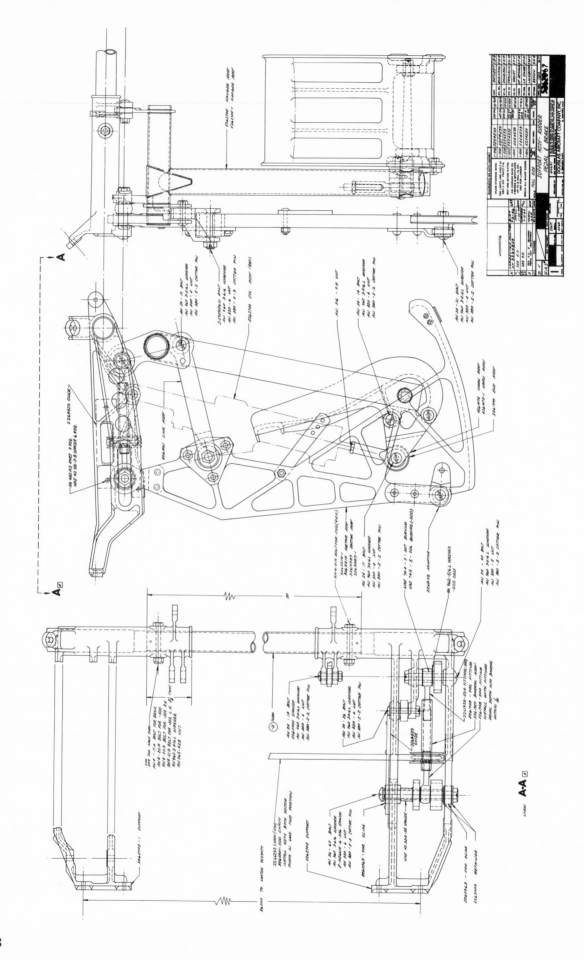

Rudder pedal

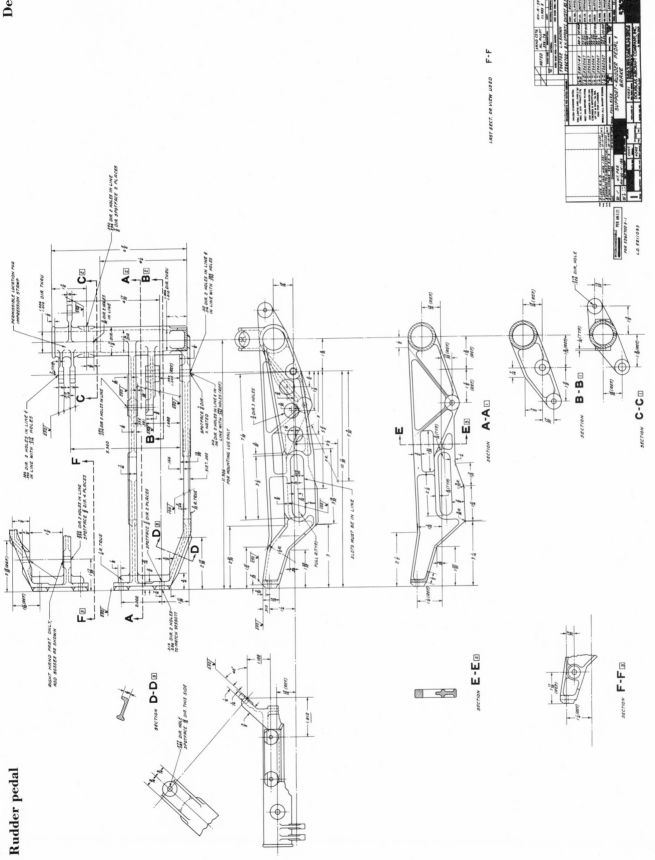

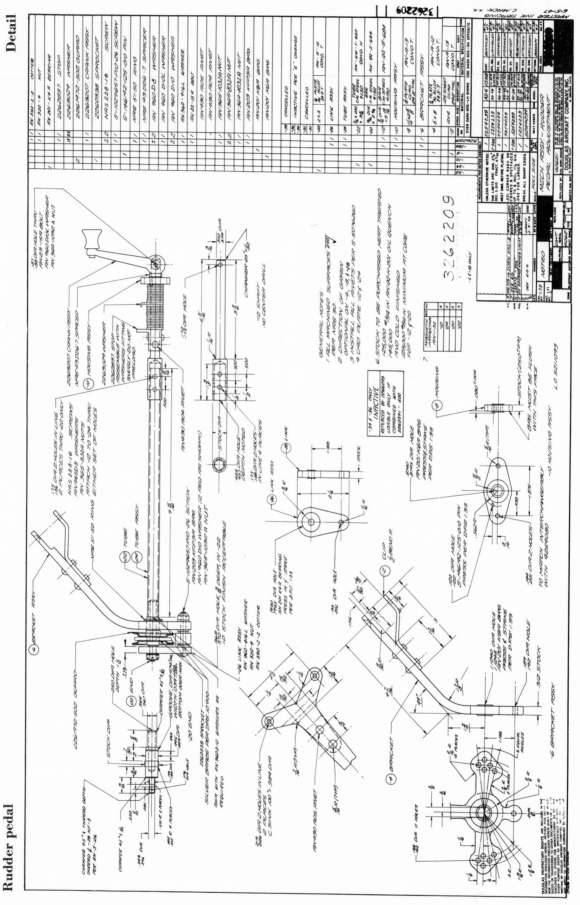

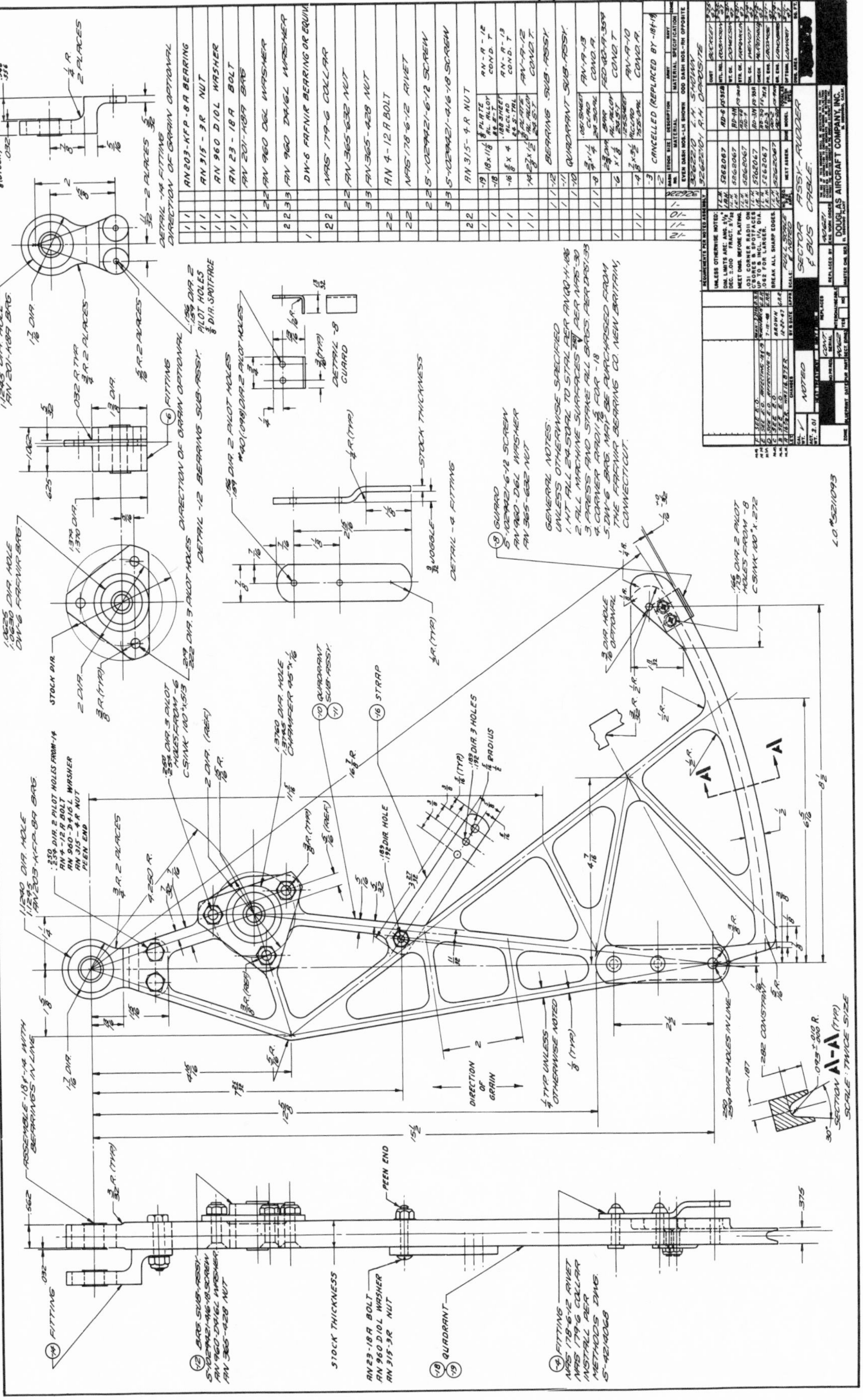

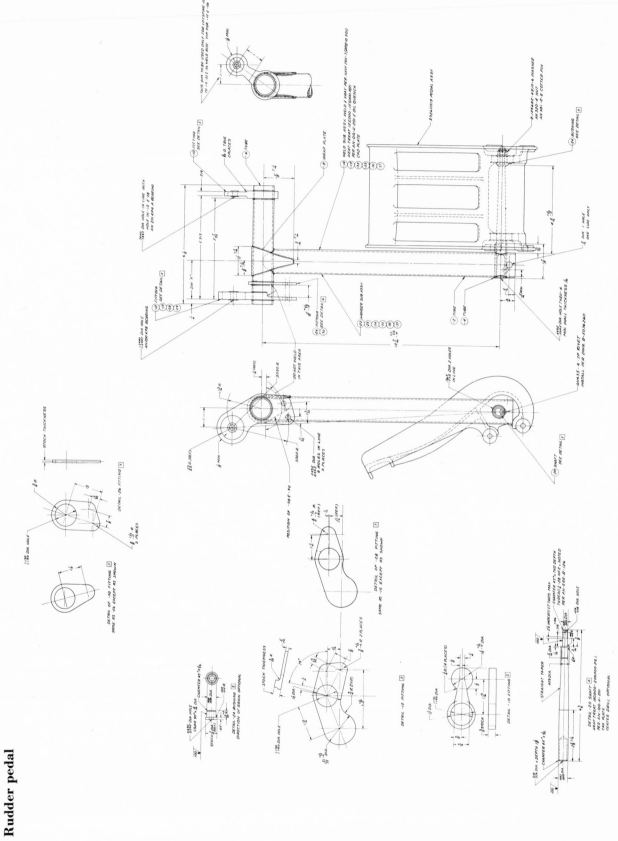

PROB. 10-18 Hinge assembly. (Fisher Body Div., General Motors Corp.)

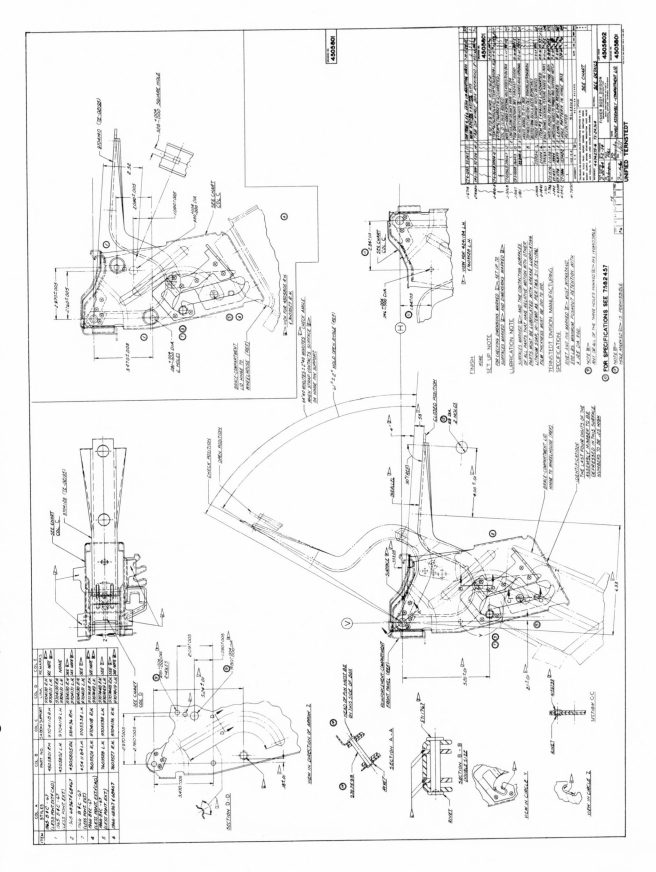

PROB. 10-19 Fuel pump. (H. Drury.)

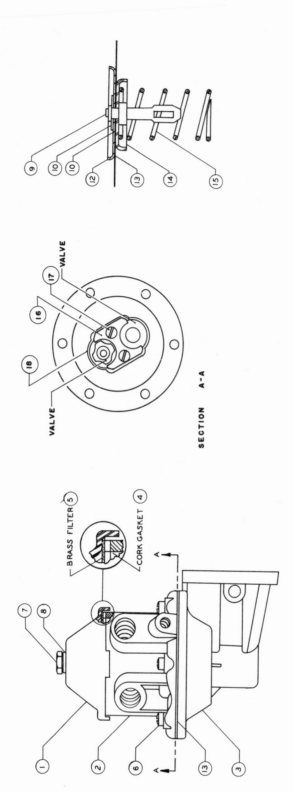

Detail

Fuel pump

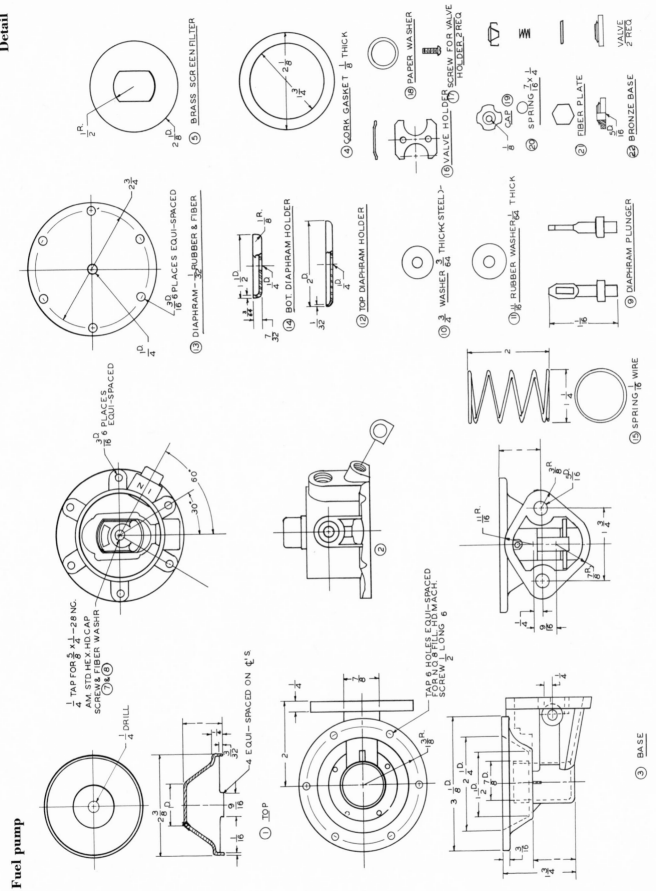

⑤ BRASS SCREEN FILTER

④ CORK GASKET ⅛ THICK

⑱ PAPER WASHER

⑯ VALVE HOLDER

⑰ SCREW FOR VALVE HOLDER, 2 REQ

⑲ CAP

⑳ SPRING ⁷⁄₁₆ × ¼

㉑ FIBER PLATE

㉒ BRONZE BASE

VALVE 2 REQ

⑬ DIAPHRAM- ¹⁄₃₂ RUBBER & FIBER

⑭ BOT. DIAPHRAM HOLDER

⑫ TOP DIAPHRAM HOLDER

⑩ WASHER ³⁄₆₄ THICK STEEL

⑪ RUBBER WASHER ¹¹⁄₆₄ THICK

⑨ DIAPHRAM PLUNGER

⑮ SPRING ¹⁄₁₆ WIRE

① TOP

③ BASE

⑦ & ⑧

BIBLIOGRAPHY

TECHNICAL ILLUSTRATION

Farmer, J. H., A. J. Hoecker, and F. F. Vavrin: *Illustrating for Tomorrow's Production,* The Macmillan Company, New York, 1950.

Gibby, Joseph: *Technical Illustration Procedures and Practices,* American Technical Society, Chicago, 1965.

Hoelscher, R. P., C. H. Springer, and R. F. Pohle: *Industrial Production Illustration,* 2d ed., McGraw-Hill Book Company, New York, 1946.

Magnam, George: *Visual Art for Industry,* Reinhold Publishing Corporation, New York, 1961.

McCartney, T. O.: *Precision Perspective Drawing,* McGraw-Hill Book Company, New York, 1963.

Pyeatt, A. D.: *Technical Illustration,* 2d ed., Higgins Ink Co., Brooklyn, 1960.

MECHANICAL DRAFTING

French, Thomas E., Carl L. Svensen: *Mechanical Drawing,* 7th ed., McGraw-Hill Book Company, New York, 1966.

Giesecke, F. E., Alva Mitchell, and H. C. Spencer: *Technical Drawing,* The Macmillan Company, New York, 1966.

Luzzander, W. J.: *Graphics for Engineers,* Prentice-Hall, Inc., Englewood Cliffs, N.J., 1962.

PROFESSIONAL MAGAZINES

Engineering Graphics
25 W. 45th St.
New York, N.Y. 10036

Industrial Art Methods
Syndicate Magazines, New York
25 W. 45th St.
New York, N.Y. 10036

Graphic Science
9 Maiden Lane
New York, N.Y. 10038

Visual Communications Instructor
Syndicate Magazines, New York
25 W. 45th St.
New York, N.Y. 10036

PROFESSIONAL ORGANIZATIONS

Technical Illustrators Management Assoc. (TIMA International), 9363 Wilshire Blvd., Beverly Hills, California 90210.

Society of Engineering Illustrators, Inc. (SEI), Rackham Memorial Bldg., 100 Farnsworth, Detroit, Michigan 48202.

Society of Technical Writers & Publishers (STWP), 1110 Vermont Ave. N.W., Suite 421, Denrike Bldg., Washington, D.C. 20005.

National Association of Industrial Artists (NAIA), Box 1346, Wheaton, Maryland 20902.

Association of Technical Artists, P. O. Box 4046, Huntsville, Alabama 35802.

GLOSSARY

airbrush A mechanical device which operates by means of air pressure, which forces prepared liquids through a nozzle spraying the liquid on various surfaces. Used extensively for photo retouching and in advertising illustration.

AN Army Navy. A method of designating standard parts.

AND Army Navy Design. A method of designating standard parts.

assembly Two or more parts attached in some manner to perform a separate function.

ATA Air Transport Association.

autopositive A trade name for various direct contact, photographic positive intermediates on paper, cloth, or film.

axonometric Isometric, dimetric, or trimetric methods of drawing.

Ben Day A screening process using dots and lines to obtain tone values and shades. Different screens are used to obtain light and dark tones.

blueline A method for making blueprints which produces a blue line on a white background.

blueprint A method for reproducing a drawing which produces a white line on a blue background.

boxing in A system used in technical illustration to draw an object with an irregular shape by drawing a box equal to the overall dimensions of the object and then cutting the box apart to form the shape of the object.

brown-line print A translucent paper or film which produces a brown line on a light background. It is used as an intermediate master to reproduce other prints.

cabinet drawing An oblique drawing using one-half the actual dimensions along the receding axis.

callout A number, a letter, or words placed on an illustration to identify the object and inform about its function.

cavalier drawing An oblique drawing with the receding axis at 45° from the horizontal.

circle projection A method used to determine angles and angle-size ellipses in technical illustration by projecting from an orthographic view.

color separation A process used to separate colors with acetate overlays used with a black plate.

continuous tone Graduated values of tones from gray to black achieved through retouched photographs, wash drawings, pencil renderings, or airbrush.

contrast Difference of tone between darker and lighter parts of an image.

coordinate construction A method of locating points on an irregular-shaped object by plotting the three dimensions along the axes of the illustration.

Cronaflex A Du Pont trade name used to designate a polyester drafting film widely used as a drawing surface in technical illustration for use with both ink and plastic pencil.

crop marks Line marks on an illustration to show the limits of the area to be reproduced. They are usually placed at each corner.

diazo paper A reproduction paper which depends on light sensitivity and is developed by exposure to ammonia fumes or an aqueous solution.

dimetric An axonometric drawing in which two of the axes make equal angles with the plane of projection.

drafting film A polyester film used as a drawing surface for ink and plastic pencil.

Drymount A heat-pressure process for fastening a drawing to mountboard by laminating a thin sheet of shellac.

exploded illustration   An illustration which shows each part of an assembly drawn separately and placed in a position that shows how the parts fit together.

eyeballing   Drawing a part approximately to shape and size using basic points as a guide—not guessing.

film positive   A positive reproduction of black lines on photographic film.

fixative   A clear solution, usually lacquer, that is sprayed on an illustration to protect lines or shading.

flow line   A line used in exploded illustrations to show how a part is assembled with another part.

flysketch   A method used by some illustration groups to show the breakdown of a subassembly, to enlarge an area, or to show alternate views by drawing a box or bracket around the parts.

foreshortened scales   Special scales used in dimetric and trimetric drawings. These scales are less than true size or foreshortened.

frisket paper   A thin paper used to cover portions of art during airbrushing.

glossy print   A type of photographic print with black lines on a glossy surface.

halftone   A method of simulating continuous tone by photographing a drawing with the use of a screen with dots to obtain variable density.

illustration board   A stiff cardboard paper material of several layers with a smooth side which is used as a drawing surface.

index number   A number or letter assigned to identify a part on an illustration and keyed to a parts list that describes the part.

intermediate   A reproduction of a drawing on translucent paper or film. It is used instead of the original drawing to reproduce other prints.

IPB   Illustrated parts breakdown abbreviation.

isometric   An axonometric drawing with all the axes at equal angles to the plane of projection. Isometric is the most frequently used method in technical illustration.

layout   An accurate plan of an illustration showing easily understood views, proper placement of parts with index numbers, leaders, and callouts to clearly identify the object.

leader   A line which extends from a part or object. It is used to identify the part by showing an index number or letter at one end of the leader.

legend   An explanation of symbols or notes that appear on an illustration.

line illustration   A technical illustration made only with lines. It contains no tonal shading.

lithography   A process of printing from a plane surface based on the mutual repulsion of water and grease.

mat   A frame of paper or cardboard used in mounting completed illustrations.

mounting   The process of placing an illustration on a stiff cardboard backing, usually with a heavy brown paper covering over a thin tissue-paper cover that protects the illustration from damage.

MS   An abbreviation for military specification.

Mylar   A Du Pont trade name for polyester film used as a drawing surface in technical illustration. (See drafting film.)

NAF   An abbreviation for Naval Aircraft Factory. A method for designating standard parts on blueprints.

NAS   An abbreviation for National Aircraft Standards. A method of designating standard parts on blueprints.

negative   A reverse-reading background copy with white lines on paper or film and a black background. Used for printing a positive.

orthographic   A multiview drawing in two dimensions rather than three, requiring several "flat" views to show the characteristics of an object.

pagination   A term used in preparation of parts catalogs. It involves the arranging of illustrations and text in proper sequence to best utilize available space.

paste-up   The work involved in preparing a finished illustration for reproduction. It includes applying index numbers, callouts, and leaders and mounting and covering.

perspective drawing   A three-dimensional drawing that shows an object as the eye sees it from one particular point. Parallel lines converge at a vanishing point.

PERT   An abbreviation for Program Evaluation Review Techniques, usually charts.

phantom   A simulated transparent surface through which normally hidden parts can be seen. An x-ray view.

photocopying   A commercial contact method for reproducing drawings.

plastic pencil   A nongraphite pencil used for drawing on drafting film.

positive   A print normally made with a negative resulting in dark lines on a light background.

register   The placing of lines on the border of a drawing. The lines are for aligning overlay sheets.

rendering   Usually refers to shading an illustration so that it will give a lifelike appearance. Various means such as pencil, ink, colors, and commercial paste-up material are used. Sometimes the word indicates any type of three-dimensional drawing.

retouching   The process of applying various gray, white, and black shades to a photograph or illustration for the purpose of clarifying, correcting, deleting, or adding emphasis.

rough drawing   Used in the first step in making an accurate illustration by mechanical means. It contains all the construction lines necessary to complete the drawing. Sometimes called the *construction drawing*.

spec   An abbreviation for the word *specification*. Usually refers to military or commercial regulations for the preparation of an illustration.

stat   An abbreviation for the word *photostat*, which is a paper negative produced by a photographic process.

Strathmore   A commercial trade name for an opaque paper used as a drawing surface.

templates   Guides used in technical illustration and made from a transparent plastic material with cutout shapes such as ellipses, hexagons, letters, numbers, and symbols.

text   The written matter on a page as opposed to drawings.

twice-up   A technical illustration term describing an illustration that is drawn twice the size that it will appear in final reproduced form.

trimetric   An axonometric drawing in which the three axes make different angles with the plane of projection. Requires three different foreshortened scales for measurements.

vellum   A translucent paper used as a drawing surface for both pencil and ink.

Varityper   A special kind of electric typewriter with interchangeable typefaces and type sizes.

waxing machine   A special machine used to apply a wax coating to illustration material in order to attach it to another surface.

xerography   A photo-offset process in which drawings, etc., are reproduced by electrostatic action.

INDEX

Notes

Notes

Notes

Notes

Notes

Notes

Notes

Notes

Notes